THE INTERNATIONAL CLUB FOR
ROLLS-ROYCE & BENTLEY OWNERS

Desk Diary 2011

pevonia®

BOTANICA
SKINCARE

| MYOXY-CAVIAR® LINE |

As time takes its toll, the aging process, environmental pollutants, unwanted toxins, free radicals and stress slowly strip away your skin's vitality and radiance. The revolutionary, de-aging **Myoxy-Caviar® Collection** with Pearl Extract effectively counteracts the imprint of time to reveal a timeless, youthful and radiant complexion.

| POWER REPAIR® LINE |

Ideal for mature skin types, **Power Repair® Line** targets wrinkles and smoothes lines with collagen, elastin, and d.n.a. Mostly comprised of creams and concentrates, the line contains the perfect age-defying solutions to hydrate and firm the face, neck, and decollete.

TARGETED
RESULTS FOR EVERY
SKIN CONCERN

pevonia
BOTANICA
LIGNE SÈVACTIVE
rejuvenating dry skin cream
50 ML ℮   NET WT. 1.7 OZ

pevonia
BOTANICA

SPA CARE FOR HIM
MYOXY-CAVIAR

baume au caviar
age-defying caviar balm
bálsamo con caviar

50 ML ℮   NET WT 1.7 OZ

PEVONIA.COM

| DRY SKIN LINE |

Pevonia's Dry Skin Line specifically delivers a potent blend of hydrating
ingredients for optimum skin health. Pear Seed Extract, Royal Jelly,
and Honey nourish, repair, and prevent moisture loss. Fine lines are
minimized, dry and dehydrated skin is relieved and revitalized.

| MEN'S LINE |

Specifically formulated to address male skincare needs and concerns, the
Pevonia Men's Line powerfully repairs and rejuvenates with Myoxy-Caviar,
Green Tea, Marine Collagen, Vitamin C and Marine Elastin. Performance
driven, it prevents razor burn and folliculitis while calming sensitivity.

YOU APPRECIATE LUXURY AND PERFORMANCE.
AS LUCK WOULD HAVE IT, SO DO WE.

Wynn Las Vegas proudly operates the largest fleet of Rolls-Royce Extended
Wheelbase Phantoms in North America.

702.770.7000 | wynnlasvegas.com

702.770.8000 | encorelasvegas.com

DISCOVER THE EXCLUSIVE EXPERIENCE THAT AWAITS YOU AS A ROLLS-ROYCE OWNER.

To those for whom luxury is a lifestyle, we invite you to explore the comfortable elegance, exciting activities and premier service of Wynn Las Vegas and Encore with the special offer below:

- Private transportation to and from the airport in a Rolls-Royce Phantom
- Two nights in an elegant Wynn Las Vegas or Encore Tower Suite
- Complimentary upgrade to a Parlor or Salon Suite (based on availability)
- A $100 Resort Credit that can be used for world-class dining, spa treatments and more
- Two passes to the Penske-Wynn Ferrari/Maserati showroom

At Wynn Las Vegas and Encore, we are privileged to have two Forbes Five Star, AAA Five Diamond rated resorts for you to enjoy with award-winning signature restaurants, an array of designer retail boutiques, two full-service spas and salons, incredible shows, an 18-hole golf course and ultra chic nightclubs and lounges.

For more information and to reserve the Rolls-Royce offer above, please call 866.770.7410 and mention code WLVRROC.

Offer valid through December 31, 2011.

Play a round of golf with friends, family, or business associates in the comfort of your own home. Link up to play friends across town or even across the world with just the push of a button. Play more than 60 unique and world renowned golf courses using your own clubs any time of day or season. The Premier Golf Simulator is truly the first class home addition for the 21st century.

(866)286-9975
www.igolfsys.com

Commercial and Residential Virtual Golf Simulators

Rolls-Royce Owners' Club
191 Hempt Road
Mechanicsburg, PA 17050

Dear Members and Enthusiasts:

This is the 14th year that the Desk Diary has been provided to RROC members as a special benefit. The Desk Diary is produced at no charge to the club with the gracious underwriting of our sponsors. Special thanks are also due to consulting editor and fellow club member Phil Brooks for his contributions to this project.

This year's edition of the RROC Desk Diary includes a number of interesting articles, including a few of historical interest regarding Rolls-Royce. The profile of Martin Cannell, an RROC member from the U.K. and a frequent contributor to the RROC Forum, highlights his family's long-time association with Rolls-Royce. Martin took his driver's license test in the family's James Young R-type, a car that was later owned by RROC past president Everett Pauls. The R-type was later passed down to Everett's son, Cortes Pauls, a current RROC director.

David Evans' article on "The Father of the Modern Rolls-Royce" is about Rupert Nicholson, who was the receiver for Rolls- Royce Ltd. when it went into bankruptcy in 1971. He was responsible for splitting the company in two with separate entities for the aero and motor car operations. He was a fascinating person and a key figure in Rolls-Royce Motor Cars' rebirth as a stand-alone company.

Phil Brooks' article on the postwar Phantoms – the Phantoms IV, V and VI – provides an interesting look at these iconic cars. Also check out the article that highlights the RROC's 2010 Annual Meet in Toronto. I hope it whets your appetite to attend the 2011 meet in Lake Tahoe, California. The Tahoe meet will start on Sunday, August 14, and end with Judging Day on Thursday, August 18th. The timing allows you to continue on to Pebble Beach for their fabulous car show on Sunday. It's a unique week of fabulous cars and scenery that should not be missed.

Be sure and mark the dates for the RROC national meet and tours in your new Desk Diary. You'll also find more national and regional events on the club's Web site, www.rroc.org. Happy motoring in 2011.

Gil Fuqua, Jr.
President, RROC

LA SAMANNA
THE RESORT IS LEGEND

La Samanna Villas | La Samanna Resort & Spa, on the beautiful island of St. Martin in the French West Indies, has long been considered one of the world's most highly acclaimed luxury resort hotels. Now, hotel owner and operator, Orient-Express, has introduced an even more exclusive opportunity. One of the most distinguished addresses in the Caribbean now offers the ultimate in Caribbean luxury villa accommodations and services.

Book one of La Samanna's eight expansive oceanfront villas and take advantage of full resort services while enjoying the privacy and comfort of a private estate. La Samanna Villas offer a simple elegance, exquisitely designed for the discerning Caribbean luxury traveler.

Spanning 7,000 square feet with sweeping 180-degree water views, each fully furnished villa features three to four master bedrooms with private balconies, indoor and outdoor dining rooms, wrap-around terraces and infinity pools.

La Samanna Villas, while private and exclusive, include direct access to the hotel's five-star services and amenities. You're provided a private concierge desk and bell stand. From VIP airport transfers, housekeeping at your villa and in-room spa treatments to private butler, maid or nanny service, there are teams ready to assist with your specific requests.

Villa owners also enjoy complete access to the amenities at La Samanna Resort — restaurants and bars, La Cave, La Samanna Spa, fitness center, tennis courts, pools, powerboat charters to neighboring islands and an on-site water sports desk.

Three-bedroom villas start at $2,000 per night, while four-bedroom villas begin at $2,500 per night.

Call **1.800.957.6128** or visit **LaSamanna.com** to learn more.

La Samanna

by ORIENT-EXPRESS

Rolls-Royce Owners' Club Desk Diary 2011
Table of Contents

Page 28

Page 34

Page 48

Page 64

Departments

AutoFocus

Page 80

Page 92

Page 108

Page 148

Touring

Finer Things

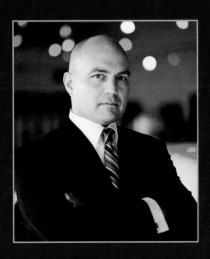

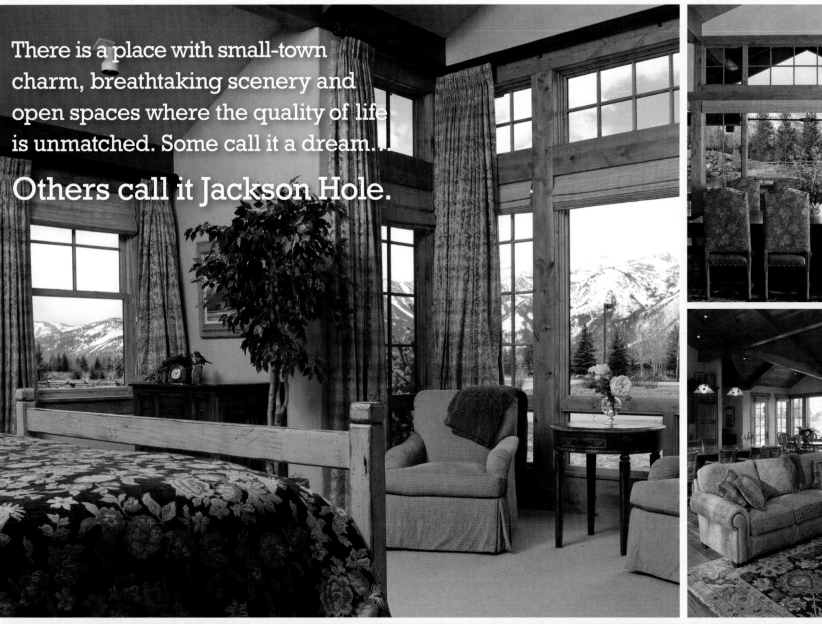

THE INTERNATIONAL CLUB FOR
ROLLS-ROYCE & BENTLEY OWNERS
Desk Diary 2011

North American Headquarters
701 North West Shore Blvd.
Tampa, FL 33609, USA
Tel. (813) 639-1900 • Fax (813) 639-4344

Publishers
Ross W. Jobson and Peter M. Antell

Chief Operating Officer
Lawrence Roberts
lawrence.roberts@faircount.com

Associate Publisher
Robin Jobson
robin.jobson@faircount.com

Controller
Robert John Thorne
robert.thorne@faircount.com

Assistant to the Publisher
Alexis Vars

Project Director
Peter Lewis
peter.lewis@faircount.com

Advertising Account Executives
Zac Cline
Geoffrey Gluck
Adam Longaker
John Perea

Office Administrator
Aisha Shazer

Chief Information Officer
John Madden
john.madden@faircount.com

Webmaster
Clyde Sanchez

IT Administrator
Anson Alexander

Sales Support
Joshua J. Roberts

Contributing Writers
Vera Marie Badertscher, Heidi Bohi
Philip C. Brooks, Craig Collins
David Evans, Colin Hughes
Claudia Jannone, R. Pierce Reid
Eric Tegler, Jan Tegler, Tara N. Wilfong

Editor in Chief
Charles Oldham
chuck.oldham@faircount.com

Consulting Editor
Philip C. Brooks

Project Editor/Senior Editor
Ana E. Lopez

Editors
Rhonda Carpenter
Iwalani Kahikina

Assistant Editor
Steven Hoarn

Art Director
Robin K. McDowall

Design and Production
Daniel Mrgan, Lorena Noya
Kenia Y. Perez-Ayala

Ad Traffic Manager
Rebecca Laborde

Executive Assistant
Lindsey Brooks

European Headquarters
5 Ella Mews, Hampstead
London NW3 2NH UK
Tel. 44 (0) 20-7-428-7000
Fax 44 (0) 20-7-284-2118

Asia-Pacific Headquarters
Lvl. 21, Tower 2, 201 Sussex Str.
Sydney NSW 2000, Australia
Tel. 61 (0) 2 9006-3370
Fax 61 (0) 2 8580-5047

Business lunch. Birthday dinner.
BE THERE.℠

There are times when your presence is needed. And then there are times when you need to be present.

The largest fleet in private aviation allows NetJets® Owners to make the most of busy, productive lives – to go almost anywhere in the world – with as little as four to ten hours notice. Superior service and unmatched flight operations mean they arrive ready to achieve or simply enjoy.

And the financial strength and commitment of Berkshire Hathaway assures the highest safety standards in the industry. These are just a few of the reasons why more individuals and corporations depend on NetJets than all other fractional aircraft companies combined.

Only NetJets™ has the resources and capability to deliver private aviation solutions that help you BE THERE.℠

NETJETS.COM | 1.877.682.3340

NETJETS® BE THERE℠

WELCOME TO PRIVATE AVIATION WITH NETJETS®

IMAGINE THE POSSIBILITIES

Picture yourself flying anywhere you want in your own private jet. You pick up the phone at any time of the day or night to arrange for a plane to take you almost anywhere. You leave when you want to leave. You fly only with people you know. You and a colleague prepare for an important presentation without worrying about who might overhear you. You avoid crowds, long lines, lost luggage, and missed connections. You arrive at an airport that is closer to your final destination, and you feel refreshed.

MAKE THE MOST OF YOUR TIME

While you can't create more time, it is possible to make the most of it. That may well be the most important reason to own a private jet. Flying with NetJets can help you seize opportunities the moment they arise, because we can get you a jet in as little as four hours and fly you to multiple cities in a single day. You can get to your final destination faster, so you

are able to spend more of your time where you want to be and less of it waiting at the airport.

THE NETJETS DIFFERENCES

Since introducing the world to the fractional aircraft ownership concept in 1986, NetJets has led the private aviation industry in everything from service and safety to the size and variety of our fleet. And the backing of Berkshire Hathaway means our financial stability is unmatched. So it's no surprise that more individuals and companies choose NetJets than all other fractional jet companies combined.

BUY AS MUCH AS YOU NEED

No matter how much or how little you fly in a year, there's a NetJets product that's right for you. Buy a fractional interest or a jet card that equals the number of hours you plan to fly in a year. Fractional interests start at 1/16 interests (50 hours of annual flying time) and include a one-time acquisition fee with predictable monthly management fees and occupied flight-hour rates. Jet cards are sold as a prepaid lease offering 25 hours of occupied flight time.

CHOOSE THE AIRCRAFT THAT FITS YOUR TRAVEL NEEDS

With NetJets, you access the largest, most diverse fleet among private aviation companies, so you can choose the jet that is right for you. If you choose to purchase a NetJets fractional interest in the NetJets U.S. program, you choose from among 11 aircraft types. If you choose to purchase a jet card, you choose from among 10 aircraft types. Regardless of the aircraft type you choose, you may also have the opportunity to exchange to another jet type.

CHANGE YOUR SENSE OF WHAT'S POSSIBLE

As the market leader in private aviation, Only NetJets™ has the size, resources, and experience to deliver the private aviation solution that best meets your needs.

FOR MORE INFORMATION CONTACT NETJETS AT:
1.877.682.3340 or VISIT WWW.NETJETS.COM

Supersports

Photo by Larry S. Glenn

AutoFocus »

Julie and Steven Solokoff arrive on the judging field in their lovely Hooper Silver Wraith limousine, LWVH116, apparently the last short-wheelbase Silver Wraith built.

Canadian summer

The 2010 RROC Annual Meet in Toronto

By Philip C. Brooks

W e passed Niagara Falls and headed for the Canadian border crossing at the Peace Bridge, wondering whether we'd get a friendly reception by the border inspectors or a very unfriendly search of the car. We'd had both before, the last being at a crossing that we hadn't realized was a training station: We were the laboratory animals there. To our delight, we were pleasantly welcomed to Canada and asked where we were going and why. We said we were headed to Markham for the RROC Annual Meet, and the inspector nodded knowingly; he'd seen other members earlier in the day. Then he got a fiendish grin on his face and said, "Well, where's your Rolls-Royce?" Sheepishly I had to admit that we had brake light problems with the car and had to bring the Mercedes. He laughed and waved us on through. Oh, the shame of it all!

On to Toronto and Markham we went, on the lovely Queen Elizabeth Highway. The countryside around Lake Ontario was very nice that summer Sunday morning, but it quickly changed from farmland to major urban metropolis as we approached Toronto. We found Markham and the meet hotel easily enough but were surprised that the hotel was in the middle of a big city – we'd expected Markham to be perhaps a little village suburb. It turned out that the suburb was actually down the road a short distance, the lovely 19th century village of Unionville. The village has a restored high street with many fun little shops and restaurants and more than one good pub. Unionville became a favorite watering hole for half of the meet attendants at one time or another, it seemed.

The meet hotel, the Hilton Suites Toronto/Markham Conference Centre & Spa (now there's a mouthful!), is a big and impressive place, with an atrium extending to the building roof, several stories up. We found the rooms reliably good and the meeting rooms extensive: Not only are there meeting rooms on the main floors of the hotel, but connected to the hotel by a bridge is a conference center with ballrooms and other facilities. The ground floor of the conference center has a covered garage, which became another favorite locale for the members. The food at the hotel was generally good and sometimes excellent throughout the meet, though the service did not quite equal the quality of the food. All in all, the Hilton at Markham was an excellent meet hotel.

Top: Dick Jaegers wonders where to park B75LE on the judging field. **Above:** Andrew Peck's Silver Wraith H.J. Mulliner sedanca de ville, WAB20, was seen in Unionville.

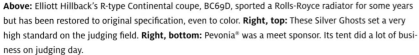

Above: Elliott Hillback's R-type Continental coupe, BC69D, sported a Rolls-Royce radiator for some years but has been restored to original specification, even to color. **Right, top:** These Silver Ghosts set a very high standard on the judging field. **Right, bottom:** Pevonia® was a meet sponsor. Its tent did a lot of business on judging day.

Toronto is vast, with great museums, galleries, shopping areas, and other attractions. We were some distance from downtown, which meant that one couldn't casually drop in to a lot of places. Fortunately, the meet had been so well organized that one had a good variety of spots to visit on the meet tours during the week. And if one just wanted to get away for a little while, there was a locally famous breakfast and lunch room in a shopping center across the highway, there was a great pub in the little shopping center next door to the hotel, and there were plenty of places in Unionville – that is, of course, if one had a chance to get away for a while; something difficult to do, as the meet calendar was full of interesting seminars and tours, along with fun dinners.

The welcoming party, sponsored by Bentley Motors, was at Angus Glen Golf Course in Markham, not far away from the meet hotel but out toward the lovely countryside. The meet committee pulled out all the stops on this event. The location was perfect, the food was very good, and the cars on display were fascinating. One such car was only seen that night at the meet: Peter Rawlings' 3-1/2-Litre Derby Bentley, a Vanden Plas drophead that he restored beautifully. We appreciated him bringing this handsome motor.

Photos by Larry S. Glenn

THE GARIA

The world's most luxurious golf car

Manufactured at the same factory as the Porsche Boxster, The Garia is built to automotive industry standards and created with meticulous attention to luxury, quality and comfort.

With The Garia, you can take on the toughest games with confidence and style. Hand-stitched seats, a built-in refrigerator from the manufacturer of refrigerators to Bentley and Rolls-Royce and an innovative golf bag holder angled at 45 degrees to enable easy access to the clubs make The Garia the most desirable golf cart on the course.

For an exceptional driving experience, The Garia features a Formula 1 inspired double wishbone front suspension and high-performance drive components from an Italian company that produces Ducati gearboxes. The aluminum profiles are made by the same company that supplies aluminum profiles to Aston Martin, Jaguar and Volvo. The elegantly designed digital instrumentation layout shows all relevant driver information.

And with The Garia LSV, a street legal version of The Garia Golf Car, versatility has never looked better. Fitted with safety equipment such as seat belts and side mirrors, The Garia LSV is allowed to be operated on public roads with a speed limit of 35 mph or less, making it an ideal second vehicle – convenient for shorter commutes or for going straight from the golf course to your favorite local café or grocery shop.

To personalize your Garia, please visit our exclusive online design center at www.garia.com/designcenter where you can choose between three standard and five upgrade colors. To complement the body color, choose between three elegant seat colors and four different rims.

At www.garia.com/finddealers you can locate your nearest dealer. For all enquiries, please contact sales@garia.com.

Top: Steve Litton brought this lovely working Silver Ghost engine for his seminar on Ghost engines.
Above: Keith and Kenneth Sherper completed a magnificent 30-plus-year restoration on their Phantom III Thrupp and Maberly drophead, 3BU86. **Right:** Bob Shaffner's Phantom III Hover/Reid pickup truck was the subject of Pierce Reid's coachbuilding seminar – and much attention.

The societies had their luncheons or dinners, as the case might be, and reports have it that all were excellent and very well attended. We went to the Derby Bentley Society dinner at 360 The Restaurant at the CN Tower and found that the Modern Car Society was having its dinner at the CN Tower as well. So were a lot of other people, as the restaurant is quite large. It seems that all roads in Canada, and perhaps all railroads as well, lead to the CN Tower; certainly they all brought a good crowd. The view from 360 Restaurant is all that one would expect, at more than 1,000 feet in the air. Both societies left very well fed and well lubricated, much appreciating the buses that brought us there. The Bentley Enthusiasts' dinner was held at the Eagle's Nest Golf Club in Richmond Hill. A well attended event, it was memorable for having four outstanding cars in the dining room along with the attendees. We were delighted to have dinner with Elliott Hillback and his gorgeous R-type Continental fastback, BC69D, which was parked about 8 feet away from our table.

We felt that one of the most interesting aspects of the 2010 Annual Meet was the variety of cars one doesn't usually see. An example would be the great selection of early postwar cars, with Mark VI Bentleys in abundance and several Rolls-Royce Silver Wraiths. We were reminded of the national meets of years ago, when those cars and the prewar cars were the staples of the club and were seen at the meets in large numbers. The sight made us start to miss our beloved old Mark VI, B96EY, the car with which we first joined the club in the 1960s. Among the really interesting prewar and early postwar cars that stood out were incredibly handsome Silver Ghosts; Danni Suskin and his 1913 open drive limousine, INA, provided rides for anyone who wanted to see what one of these wonderful cars is all about.

Top: Ned Numata arrives at the meet hotel in his Springfield Silver Ghost Pickwick, S183ML. **Right:** The two factories' lineup of current models on the judging field was more than impressive.

There was a delightful variety of Phantom IIIs and Derby Bentleys as well, with several just-restored cars making their debuts: The Sherpers' Phantom III Thrupp and Maberly drop-head, 3BU86, was parked next to Andrew Davidson's Phantom III Binder sedanca de ville, 3BU94. Both were fresh out of very long restorations, and the efforts expended were worth it: Those two cars were utterly magnificent. Nearby was Mermie Karger's Phantom III Gurney Nutting sports saloon, 3DL122, aka "Ovid," which she and her husband, Colin Hughes, drove at the end of the meet to Pebble Beach.

One old friend that had disappeared for decades was B180JD, the ex-Sam Shoup Gurney Nutting streamlined 4-1/4 coupe, now owned and beautifully restored by Andrew Davidson.

Photos by Larry S. Glenn

Left: Akin Davis' Mark VI Freestone and Webb drophead, B76AK, emerged from a very long restoration and wowed all. What a swoopy car! **Right:** Wendell Smith brought his handsome Phantom I Windovers allweather, 83EF, to Toronto: another car emerging from a long restoration.

Another old friend that was good to see again was the Mark VI standard steel saloon, B296PV, which our meet chairs, Henry and Susan Popp, have cherished for years. Perhaps the most delightful surprise was another car that quietly snuck onto the judging field, Akin Davis' Mark VI Freestone and Webb drophead, B76AK, fresh from the restoration shop after nearly a decade there. A rarity of rarities was Michael Browning's Mark VI Vanden Plas saloon, B17AJ, of which only a handful were built before Vanden Plas was bought by Austin and started to build Princess cars; it was a real treat to see this handsome and unusual car. We were charmed by HP383, a 3-Litre Vanden Plas tourer driven to the meet by its owner, David Howe, who drove the car from Nova Scotia. The car was well set up for touring, and David reported having a very pleasant drive of well over 1,000 miles. He clearly had

a good time at the meet, for he will be one of the hosts for a forthcoming Nova Scotia RROC tour.

One of the most interesting vehicles at the meet was a pickup truck. It was not any old pickup truck but was a Phantom III, 3DL70, which belongs to Bob Shaffner. Bob had bought and restored the chassis, the rear of the original body having gone away long ago. Then he worked with Pierce Reid and Billings Cooke at the Vintage Garage to mate the front of the body up to a Ford pickup bed with what amounted to a new coachbuilt body. Pierce gave an interesting and popular Foundation Lecture on "Coachbuilding in the 21st Century," using this very handsome P-III as an example on display in the lobby of the convention center. The vehicle was the center of attention all week, and it was generally felt that the truck was so good that Bubba need not apply to drive it!

The collection of prewar and postwar Silver Ghosts was utterly stunning, and the Phantoms I, II, and V were quite splendid. The small horsepower cars formed a very interesting array, as did the early postwar cars. We particularly liked Andrew Peck's Mulliner Silver Wraith sedanca de ville, WAB20, but we would have happily driven any of those cars home. The Clouds, Shadows, Spirits, and Spurs were there in delicious droves, as were their Bentley cousins, and several of the newer Rolls-Royces and even more of the newer Bentleys were present. We were intrigued by the large numbers of very fast postwar Bentleys in attendance: Clearly a lot of members wanted to cover the distance to Toronto quickly.

Judging was held at Milne Park in Markham, not far from the meet hotel. We fear that our navigation skills

Andrew Davidson's 4-1/4 Gurney Nutting coupe, B180JD, was once owned by club founder Sam Shoup. It disappeared for years but emerged beautifully restored.

weren't on target that morning, and we did rather lead Rick Barrett and his lovely car all round Robin Hood's barn to get there. It was worth the drive, though, for the cars present were a stunning collection of nearly 100 years of Rolls-Royce and Bentley motoring. Milne Park was a perfect setting for judging, with plenty of space to spread out and shade during the hours when needed. It started off as a lovely day but turned rainy just as things were wrapping up.

The final banquet, sponsored by Rolls-Royce Motor Cars, was, of course, where all the awards were announced. It was held at the Hilton Suites and was done to a very high standard: Both the food and service were excellent. Unfortunately, rains had come to Toronto late in the afternoon, and plans for the drive-by were washed away. Still, it was a lovely evening and a fine wrap-up to a very pleasant Canadian summer week.

The 2010 Annual Meet is best characterized as friendly and convivial. It was not so huge that one got lost in the crowd, but it was big enough to ensure real variety and a delightful time for all the attendees. The Toronto area is friendly, too, and we'd love to come back and see more of it. Thanks to Henry and Susan Popp and their committee for a job very well done.

The new Bentley Mulsanne has met with favorable reception since its introduction in 2009.

A Year of Growth

By Philip C. Brooks

2010 has been a year of growing sales, both for the factory at Chichester and for the factory at Crewe. It's also been a year of excitement, as the new models introduced last year entered the marketplace in a major way.

At the Bentley factory, it was reported that over 46,000 Bentley Continentals had been built from introduction of the Continental GT coupe in 2002 through the middle of 2010. About half of these cars sold over the past eight years, or a bit over 22,000 units, were the coupes; the remainder was split among the GTC convertible, the Flying Spur sedan, the GT Speed models, and the GT Supersports coupe. Limited edition models for specific markets were introduced:

the "Arabia," the "China," and the "80-11" for the North American market. Furthermore, the new Mulsanne, introduced at Pebble Beach in 2009, came online to great praise worldwide. This year the "Bespoke" or custom orders are being called "Series 51," named after 1951 when John Blatchley set up the official Styling Department at Crewe.

Sales totaled some 9,500 units in 2008, with North American sales comprising 29.5 percent of that total. Sales dropped in 2009, as economies worldwide became shakier, but have rebounded vigorously in 2010. The factory at Crewe is working at capacity as demand for all the Bentley models increases.

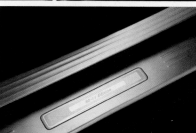

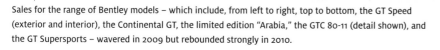

Sales for the range of Bentley models – which include, from left to right, top to bottom, the GT Speed (exterior and interior), the Continental GT, the limited edition "Arabia," the GTC 80-11 (detail shown), and the GT Supersports – wavered in 2009 but rebounded strongly in 2010.

This photo: The current Rolls-Royce stable includes, from left to right, the Phantom Coupé, the Phantom sedan, the Ghost sedan, and the Phantom Drophead. **Below, left and right:** So far in 2010, Ghosts have consistently been sold out three months in advance.

All models will be built with FlexFuel technology in 2011, enabling them to run on gasoline, ethanol (including E85), or a combination of the two. The lineup of Bentley products is exciting now; with the introduction of a new Continental GT coupe with revised styling and enhanced performance, the lineup will be even more exciting in 2011. Rumors abound of a Continental coupe with a smaller V-8 engine in addition to the new GT coupe: Only time will tell about that.

At the Rolls-Royce factory, growth has also been steady. From the first few hundred Phantom sedans produced in 2003, production figures have risen steadily. In 2007, the factory sold 1,010 units; in 2008, they sold 1,212 units; and in 2009 they experienced a sales drop and sold 1,002 units, including the first few new Ghosts to be sold. So far, in 2010 production of both Phantoms and Ghosts has been consistently sold out three months in advance, and the 2010 sales target is to double the 2009 sales figure. 2,004 units sold in

2010 will be a significant leap forward for Rolls-Royce, but it's likely that the factory will reach that total: For the first six months of 2010, sales were up 200 percent over the first six months in 2009. By June of 2010, the factory was producing 15 cars a day.

Current models available from Chichester include the Phantom sedan, the Phantom Extended Wheelbase sedan, the Phantom Drophead, the Phantom Coupé, and the new Ghost sedan. It's worth noting that well over half of the cars built at Chichester now are "Bespoke" models, special order cars with custom paint, trim, accessories, and the like. In fact, in 2009 nearly all Phantoms were Bespoke cars. The Bespoke options are proving nearly as attractive to Ghost purchasers as they are to Phantom purchasers.

The Ghost sedan is a smaller car than the Phantom, but it is hardly a small car. It can be equated in some ways to the old days of Rolls-Royce, when Rolls-Royce Ltd. built both a big car and a little car: the Phantom II and the 20/25, for instance, or the Phantom V and the Silver Cloud and S-series. The Phantom from Chichester is a very big car, not unlike the Phantoms of old in size and status, whereas the new Ghost is just a big car not unlike the small horsepower cars and Clouds in comparative size and status. Thus the new Rolls-Royce factory has returned to the big car-little car model of old.

North America is by far the largest market for both Rolls-Royce and Bentley. For example, in 2009, when the U.S. economy was worrisome, Rolls-Royce sales in the United States accounted for 33 percent of sales worldwide. Bentley sales were not far behind as a percentage of sales, but nearly 10 times greater in terms of numbers of units sold. It's not surprising that both factories continue to realize that the Rolls-Royce and Bentley clubs worldwide, and especially in North America, are their best rolling advertisement.

That being the case, it's easy to understand the companies' willingness to bring their latest offerings to our club's events and to let members drive the cars. Driving these cars is a real privilege, and we are deeply grateful to both companies for their generosity in letting all of us do so. Members had wonderful opportunities to drive Bentley Continental Speed and Supersports models at the Orlando Inter-Regional Meet and at the Toronto Annual Meet. We can report that there are few things more exciting than taking a Supersports coupe out on the highway, be it in Florida or Ontario! And we had great opportunities to drive Rolls-Royce products at those meets and on the Fall Tour in upstate New York. Having driven two Ghosts now, one in the rain and snow at Lake Placid, I have to say that I have rarely driven a nicer and, in its own way, more practical road car than the new Ghost. We'll all hope to try a Mulsanne next year!

To sum up, 2010 has been a year of growth in products and in sales at both factories. Each factory offers a very attractive choice of highest-end luxury sedans and convertibles, and buyers who are willing to spend between $200,000 and $450,000 are lined up to purchase these cars. The two factories are carving out slightly different niches for themselves. Rolls-Royce dominates the upper end of the very big luxury car market, while Bentley dominates the sporting end of that market. Rolls-Royce is successfully following Lord Hives' statement about building "the best car in the world that we can sell," while Bentley is equally successfully following W.O.'s original goal to build "a good car, a fast car, the best in its class." Who could ask for more than that?

DESTINY? IMAGINATION? CAUSALITY?

This fabulous Estate could well be the Retreat you've always dreamed of … Just give it a look!

12 Bedrooms ✦ 14 Baths ✦ Sleeps 28 + Staff • Main House is 11,000 sq ft ✦ Lot size 10 Acres ✦ 355 ft. of beachfront property
SAADET ESTATE on World renowned Grace Bay Beach - Emerald Point - Providenciales - TURKS & CAICOS ISLANDS

SAADET HOUSE

A magnificent beachfront Estate comprising a main residence, a four-bedroom guesthouse, a separate staff house and gatehouse. The main property is set on 10 acres with 355 feet of white sand beach frontage, on the most secluded beach of Providenciales. In addition, the property also includes a protected canal lot suitable for dockage or a boathouse with immediate access to the protected "Leeward Going Through Channel."

Designed for luxurious indoor and outdoor living, the two-story main residence comprises 11,000 square feet of truly opulent interior living and dining areas with a large screened Florida room facing the expansive pool deck and the pristine beach beyond.

In total, the main residence includes: 7 bedrooms, 9 bathrooms, 3 independent master closets, Owner's ample Private Office, a massage and fitness room with direct access from the two main master bedrooms and adjoining hallway. An elevator provides easy access to the 2nd floor.

Nearly 10,000 square feet of covered verandah and terraces complete the house, which boasts a 5,000-square-foot swimming pool deck surrounding the majestic 77,000-gallon swimming pool with 2 independent large Jacuzzis; all set in manicured gardens with lush tropical landscaping.

ADDITIONAL AMENITIES INCLUDE:

- All Glass Doors and windows Hurricane Proof to Miami Dade County Code.
- A TV lounge and home theatre.
- Flat-panel TV's, HI-FI, independent A/C and fans in each Ambiance and rooms.
- Guest Cottages providing 4 oversized en suite bedrooms each with private bathrooms and screened terraces.
- Independent Staff Accommodation for 6.
- Closed-circuit security video cameras, VOIP Tel System, wired Internet and Wi-Fi.
- A large commercial-sized kitchen fully equipped with Monogram Appliances.
- Independent laundry room.

- A vast 3,000-square-foot white tiled basement provides more than ample storage, alongside the electrical, water pump, and pool pump rooms and dedicated Owner's Private Storage Room.
- 2 Cisterns, 10,000 + 50,000 Gallons, for house and irrigation use.
- A backup generator provides assurance in case of power outage.
- Covered parking for 11 cars - Garages for 4 other cars.
- R.O. Water plants - Two Klagester sewage treatment plants.
- Fully automatic irrigation system.
- Only a 5 minute drive to 18-hole Golf Course - 10 minutes to the Center of Grace Bay for Shopping and Restaurants - 20 minutes to the International and Private Jets Airports - possibility to build a helicopter landing platform on site - Just a 2 minute walk to your future Dock.

For more information please call: 1 305 790 3063 ♦ 1 649 331 7777 ♦ 1 649 331 7225 or E-MAIL: saadet@tciway.tc

www.turksdreamhouse.com

Phantoms in a Postwar World

By Philip C. Brooks

In early 1945, Rolls-Royce placed a "teaser" advertisement in British motoring publications: "In due course the post-war Rolls-Royce will make its appearance. It will uphold the fame and prestige of its predecessor. When circumstances permit, a further statement will be made regarding prices and deliveries."

Above the text was an illustration of a car – perhaps an H.J. Mulliner-bodied Phantom III sedanca de ville, or perhaps a hint of a postwar car. Taking the illustration and the text into account, one could have assumed that a postwar Phantom would be built. Maybe it would – but maybe it would not.

In July 1938, Rolls-Royce had to place an ad denying rumors that the Phantom III would be shortly replaced by an eight-cylinder Phantom. However, in 1939, an experimental car built as part of the development program for the "Rationalized Range" of motor cars appeared to be a replacement for the Phantom III. This was 30-G-VII, a Rolls-Royce with a Park Ward seven-

The Aga Khan's Phantom IV sedanca de ville by Hooper, 4AF20, now owned by Bob Shaffner.

Rolls-Royce's "teaser" ad from 1945. Promises, promises....

passenger limousine body, fitted with the straight eight cylinder version of the new "B" series "Rationalized Range" engine. This car, affectionately known as "Big Bertha," was officially called the "Silver Phantom."

An eight-cylinder engine was also fitted to a Mark V Bentley as part of the testing program. This car had formidable performance and quickly became known as "Scalded Cat." It played a pivotal role in the decision to build a Phantom successor to the Phantom III.

At the end of World War II, the factory decided to go ahead with two six-cylinder models in the proposed "Rationalized Range": the Mark VI Bentley, available either with the factory's first standard steel saloon body or with coachbuilt bodies, and the Silver Wraith Rolls-Royce, available only for coachbuilt bodies. Rolls-Royce felt that economic conditions were not right for introduction of a new Phantom with the eight-cylinder engine. That car would have to wait.

However, in 1948, Prince Philip, Duke of Edinburgh, heard about Scalded Cat and asked if he might test it out. The Duke enjoyed the car immensely. When he returned the car, he apparently murmured about how nice it would be to have a car with performance in the Royal Mews. On November 15, 1948, not long after Prince Philip's fun with Scalded Cat and the day after Prince Charles was born, an order came through for a Rolls-Royce motor car for Their Royal Highnesses Princess Elizabeth and Prince Philip. Such a car would have to meet their official needs, which meant it must be a limousine. It would have to have good performance, especially since Prince Philip intended to drive it a lot. The car would be the first official Rolls-Royce in the stables.

The factory seized on this opportunity to build the first Phantom IV. It was originally planned to be the only Phantom IV, a strictly one-off car. It would be built on the postwar chassis design, with a wheelbase of 145 inches, and would use the eight-cylinder version of the new engine. H.J. Mulliner was selected as the coachbuilder, and they prepared drawings for approval. The chassis, 4AF2, was delivered to Mulliner in July of 1949 for erection of the body, and Prince Philip visited Mulliner more than once while the car was being built. When the car was delivered to Clarence House in July of 1950, Princess Elizabeth was delighted with the car and felt that it was "a magnificent example of British craftsmanship."

The car was painted dark Valentine Green, with green leather and grey cloth interior, and had a silver mascot of St. George slaying the dragon. (The mascot was extensively tested at Crewe for stability.) 4AF2 had adjustable front seats; a rear seat that could be raised; a transparent roof panel; electrically operated windows, rear window blind, and division; a radio in the rear armrest; three heaters; face-forward occasional seats; and a curly mohair floor rug with silk pile border in the rear compartment. When Princess Elizabeth ascended to the throne in 1952, the car was repainted in the royal colors of claret and black, and the front upholstery was redone in dark blue cloth. An automatic gearbox was fitted in 1955. HM the Queen still has the car, to which she has referred fondly as "my old Rolls." 4AF2 caused a sensation, and its appearance in the Royal Mews sounded the death knell for Daimler as the royal car.

About the time that 4AF2 was ordered, Crewe received an order for three cars for Generalissimo Francisco Franco of Spain: two heavily armored limousines and a convertible sedan. These heavy cars would have overburdened the Silver Wraith chassis, so the factory decided to build the cars as Phantom IVs – especially since the Foreign Office suggested that Crewe could not turn down the order. The coachwork order was placed with H.J. Mulliner, who would supply their "standard"

Princess Margaret's Phantom IV by H.J. Mulliner, 4BP7, formerly owned by Bob Shaffner.

armor plating. Unfortunately, the Spanish military tested a sample of this armor plating and shot bullet holes through it. The English Steel Corporation supplied alternative plating, which was shot full of holes by Bill Allen of the Crewe design staff. The Spanish government then supplied samples of the desired armor plating, and English Steel modified their product accordingly. So far, the cars have not been shot up! These cars, limousines 4AF14 and 4AF16 and cabriolet 4AF18, were delivered in 1952 and remain today with the Spanish royal family.

Other Phantom IVs were built by this time. The second Phantom IV was 4AF4, the factory's delivery lorry/experimental vehicle. It had a handsome front body section by Park Ward and a pick-up bed behind, and it was fast enough – 90 mph – that Rolls-Royce drivers caught the beady eyes of the constabulary. It was dismantled at the end of 1963.

The third Phantom IV, 4AF6, was ordered by the Shah of Iran with a very modern H.J. Mulliner drophead body. It was delivered at the end of 1951, well before the three Spanish cars that had been ordered in 1948. The body of 4AF6 was too flexible, and the car was dismantled in 1959. The body was later fitted to Phantom III 3BT15 and caused much interest at a West Coast RROC annual meet some years ago.

The fourth Phantom IV was 4AF8, built for the Emir of Kuwait, a handsome Mulliner saloon without division. It was delivered in September 1951, and the Emir was pleased enough with it that he later ordered two more Phantom IVs.

4AF10 was the first Phantom IV to be bodied by a firm other than H.J. Mulliner. HRH Prince Henry, the Duke of Gloucester, chose Hooper to build a body to his exacting specifications. The Duke and his family had recently returned from several years in Australia, where he served

Top: 5AS95, Phantom V James Young sedanca de ville, design BV22SD, owned by Charles Bronson. The canework is original. **Above:** 5AT48 is a James Young Phantom V limousine, design PV10M, hearkening back to that coachbuilder's earlier designs on Silver Wraiths, Silver Dawns, and R-types. The car is owned by Bill Borchert.

as Governor General, and the three Rolls-Royces that he had taken with him had accumulated great mileages. Replacements were needed, as the Duke and Duchess undertook many official engagements. Prince Henry had definite preferences in his motor cars, going back to his cars in the late 1920s; he favored Weymann bodies with their matte finishes, separate side and spot lights, and plain rather than figured wood trim. 4AF10 was designed by Hooper with twin sidemounts, matte black body panels and gloss black wings, separate side and spot lights, plain

walnut trim, a full leather interior, and face-forward occasional seats. The car also had a pneumatically inflated rear seat, a mohair rear carpet overlay similar to that on 4AF2, louvres over the door windows for ventilation, double glazing on the side windows, and sliding purdah panels for the rear quarter windows. The car was very imposing. It was also huge, and the late HRH Prince William of Gloucester told me that the family sold the car because it was too big. Delivered in September 1951, it was sold in October 1960 and is still in the U.K. The Duke and Duchess also ordered a Silver Wraith, ALW10, one of the first long-wheelbase Silver Wraiths, in November 1951; it had the same basic Hooper body design as 4AF10, with many of the same features and paint scheme. It was delivered in September 1952, and the Duke and Duchess kept it until the late 1960s. By this time, they had been driving their James Young Phantom V, 5AT30, for several years; it had replaced the Phantom IV and it met their needs very well. HRH Prince Richard, the current Duke of Gloucester, has used 5AT30 for many years.

Phantom IVs were ordered by other members of the British royal family and heads of state. The factory decided, apparently unofficially, that the Phantom IV would be reserved for royalty and heads of state. There was discussion of building Phantom IV cars for private customers, and coachbuilders' drawings exist for proposed cars for such good customers as Briggs Cunningham and James Melton. However, those orders never came about.

One other car was built, in a way, for internal use. This was 4AF12, a Hooper seven-passenger limousine for Lord Hives, Rolls-Royce managing director, upon his elevation to the peerage. Crewe sold it to Princess Marina, Duchess of Kent, in 1954, and she used the car for many years.

A very special Phantom IV, 4BP5, was built for use by HM the Queen. Known as "Jubilee," it was a state landaulette by Hooper and was perfect for parade occasions. It was built with the same internal dimensions as those on the Daimler state landaulettes still in the Royal Mews. Rolls-Royce loaned the car to the Palace at first, but the Palace bought it in 1959 along with two new Phantom Vs. It was displayed in the museum at Sandringham for several years and is now on display at the Hunt House.

Club member Bob Shaffner has owned two Phantom IVs over the years and has displayed them at the Rolls-Royce Foundation museum and at annual meets. One is 4AF20, a curvaceous Hooper sedanca de ville that was originally ordered by the Aga Khan. The other is 4BP7, a Mulliner limousine originally ordered by Princess Margaret. Another Phantom IV, 4BP3, was owned by member Bill Davis for many years. It's a Hooper "Empress Line" limousine originally ordered by the Prince Regent of Iraq and is one of the most beautiful of that body style built. Its body proportions are so good that it's difficult to tell how large it is. All three of these cars are stunning.

The Phantom IV ceased production in 1956, after two more cars were delivered to the Emir of Kuwait and one more to the Shah of Iran. Eighteen cars were built altogether. By this time, the Phantom IV was not considered necessary for state use: Appropriate bodies had been built on Silver Wraiths, including a Hooper convertible sedan for Nubar Gulbenkian that was used at the wedding of Prince Rainier and Princess Grace. Another convertible sedan was built for the King and Queen of Greece. State landaulettes were built, one for Emperor Haile Selassie of Ethiopia and others for use by governors-general. It was very possible to buy a Silver Wraith for state occasions, which worked well for the factory: Building a Phantom IV chassis proved to be a demanding and disrupting process.

Right: The rear compartment of 5BX38 shows James Young's craftsmanship at its understated best. **Far right:** Phantom V James Young limousine 5BX38, design PV22, is James Young at their styling apex. The car belongs to the Rolls-Royce Foundation.

Rolls-Royce was hardly done with Phantoms, though. The factory announced a new model, the Phantom V, and showed examples at the 1959 auto shows. This car had the Silver Cloud chassis, lengthened to 145 inches, and the new V-8 engine. It was practical to build profitably, which was more than could be said for Phantom IVs. Rolls-Royce built 516 Phantom Vs over the next nine years. In 1962, mechanical improvements were incorporated into the Phantom V, along with four head-lights. At the same time, the upper half of the body received a more steeply angled windscreen and more razor-edged rear lines to the roof, rear quarter, and boot lines. The effect was more in the tradition of Mulliner.

Two Phantom Vs were built for HM the Queen. 5AS33 and 5AT34 were ordered by Buckingham Palace to update the royal fleet. Both had Perspex rear roofs, so that the royal family could be seen in inclement weather, and removable folding metal covers for privacy when desired. 5AS33 was delivered first, in 1960, with 5AT34 following in 1961. The two cars were the prime transport for the royal family for many years, with the two Phantom IVs acting as back-up vehicles. Known by their factory code names as "Canberra I" and "Canberra II," they still belong to the Queen.

The most commonly seen Phantom V has a timeless seven-passenger body, first built by Park Ward and later by H.J. Mulliner, Park Ward, after the amalgamation of the two firms. The factory also wanted to offer a five-passenger touring limousine, in order to compete with James Young's seven-passenger and five-passenger limousines. H.J. Mulliner had designed and built a five-passenger Phantom V, which was rather graceful and looked something like a very large Bentley Continental Flying Spur. However, Rolls-Royce wanted to start integrating Mulliner and Park Ward, so they squelched the Mulliner five-passenger car and had Mulliner build a series of eight cars that were a combination of Mulliner and Park Ward coachwork. These cars were Phantom V chassis delivered to Mulliner with Park Ward bodies up to the beltline, the idea being that Mulliner would build a five-passenger body with a Mulliner razor-edge rear and Mulliner interior. The staff at Mulliner was not happy with this arrangement, but they produced a very handsome car. Members John and Sandy Matsen own 5LAT86, a car shown at Earl's Court and then delivered to its Oklahoma owner. The order took over two years to fulfill, but the end product was worth the wait.

Other designs were offered as well. Park Ward's state landaulette, modified by H.J. Mulliner, Park Ward after the merger, became a popular offering over the years. Hooper built a test mule for the Phantom V and then one seven-passenger limousine body, which they displayed at Earl's Court in 1959, and then went out of business. Member John Haulmark owns that car; it's handsome but very different from other coachbuilders' styling. Chapron built two limousines to Hooper designs.

The epitome of razor-edge, swept-tail styling was achieved by James Young on the Phantom V chassis, with their PV15 seven-passenger limousine and their PV22 five-passenger touring limousine. Designer "Mac" McNeil evolved his earlier James Young designs to reach an elegance of line that has yet to be surpassed, and the length of the Phantom V chassis gave him a frame that he needed. These cars were breathtaking when new, especially when painted in the slightly metallic James Young Midnight Blue, an effect reached through the use of cuttlefish scale. They remain breathtaking today.

H.J. Mulliner, Park Ward built cars for HM the Queen, a landaulette for HRH the Queen Mother, and state landaulettes for other people. James Young built a few sedancas de ville, one of which had canework sides, and all of which were distinguished. They also built special variants of their standard designs, including several with small rear windows and a very special limousine for HRH the Duke of Gloucester; it has a matte finish over much of its body and freestanding R-100 headlamps. Additionally, they built two coupes.

However, the writing was on the wall for James Young as Rolls-Royce switched over from the Silver Cloud and S series cars with separate chassis to the Silver Shadow and T series monocoque cars. James Young modified 50 Silver Shadow and T saloons into coupes, but these cars came out looking rather squared-off and were extremely expensive to build. In 1967, feeling that they could not stay in business building only a limited number of Phantoms, James Young closed their doors. Only Mulliner Park Ward, as now known, remained in the coachbuilding business.

Mulliner Park Ward had plenty of work building the Silver Shadow and T coupes and convertibles, the Phantom V, and,

FORGIATO

Rolls-Royce Drophead w/ 24" Piastra

Ritorno   Otto   Alneato   Fiore

Forgiato wheels are custom built 3-piece forged wheels made of 6061-t6 aerospace grade aluminum. They are all custom built to fit any Rolls-Royce. Visit our website to see more designs and build your own wheel with any combination of colors and finishes you can imagine. Forgiato.com | 818-351-1171

Above: 5LAT86 is a handsome Phantom V H.J. Mulliner touring limousine, design 7516, and very different from the Park Ward limousine. It belongs to John Matsen. **Right:** The interior fittings of 5LAT86, with appropriate "goodies" by H.J. Mulliner.

as of 1968, the new Phantom VI. The Phantom VI was very much a continuation of the Phantom V but with mechanical modifications and some body redesign. The Phantom VI was in production, in numbers that grew more limited over the years, until 1992.

The prototype Phantom VI was built in 1966, with production commencing in 1968. Mechanically, the car used the Silver Shadow V-8 engine, with its improved cylinder heads, along with separate air-conditioning for front and rear seats. The same chassis was retained, with a wheelbase of 145 inches. A new dash was introduced, incorporating the "eyeball" air-conditioning outlets introduced a few years earlier. The "Alpha" version, which was armored, was introduced in 1969, and the car was made compliant with European safety standards in 1972. The Phantom VI was not submitted for federal crash tests and was never sold new in the United States. One car was delivered new under diplomatic protection to the British ambassador to the United Nations; he kindly displayed the car at the 1978 RROC Williamsburg Meet. Several other cars have been brought into the United States in recent years.

In 1978, the bigger version of the V-8, at 6,750 cc, became standard on the Phantom VI, along with the GM 400 three-speed gearbox and the Silver Shadow-type braking system. This braking system had to be employed because the GM 400 gearbox could not be used with the old servo brake. HM the Queen's Silver Jubilee car was the first car built to the new specifications. These specifications became standard for the rest of the Phantom VI production run. There were a total of 374 Phantom VIs built over 26 years – far and away the longest production run of any Phantom model.

Two Phantom VIs were built for the Queen. The first was PGH101, the first "Alpha" version car, built as a Silver Jubilee present from the Society of Motor Manufacturers and Traders and known as "Oil Barrel." It was built to much the same specifications as the two "Canberra" Phantom Vs, including fitting the Perspex roof, but with the "Alpha" mechanical improvements. It had four headlights and, because of safety regulations, forward-hinged rear doors. The second Phantom VI was PMH10415, code named "Lady Norfolk," built with a standard roof but longer quarter windows and a glass insert over the rear seat. We saw the car being built at Mulliner Park Ward's Hythe Road works in 1986 and recognized it as being very unusual. It was quite handsome with its larger quarter windows and looked very Mullineresque. In fact, this car was designed, as were the earlier Phantom VI and the two Phantom Vs, by Park Ward's designer, Peter Wharton. Wharton joined Park Ward in 1934, retired in 1979, and was coaxed happily out of retirement in 1985 to design "Lady Norfolk." The car was delivered to Her Majesty in 1987 and is still in use today.

HM the Queen's cars are painted in royal claret and black. All have removable bumpers so that they could fit in the garage aboard the royal yacht *Britannia*, and all carry the St. George mascot when the Queen is in the car.

Top: John Ellison's Phantom V State Landaulette, 5LVF113, originally ordered by the Romanian government, which failed to take delivery. When the car was owned by Erle Heath, it was used by HM the Queen on state visits to Bermuda and the Cayman Islands. **Above:** John Ellison's Phantom VI Mulliner, Park Ward limousine, PRH4703, has a very different rear treatment to a Mulliner or a Park Ward Phantom V limousine. The rear quarter panels and boot are decidedly Mulliner, but the rear lights are quite different.

Phantom V and Phantom VI landaulettes are very special cars. Designed as parade cars for heads of state, they were built over the production run of the two models, with one of the first being for HM the Queen Mother and now used by HRH the Prince of Wales. Body designs varied, some with a fully opening roof over the rear compartment and others with an opening roof over the rear seat. Each car was somewhat different, particularly in the rear compartment. One of these cars, now owned by member John Ellison, was a Phantom V ordered by the Romanian government for use by President Ceausescu, but the order was cancelled. Late club member Erle Heath owned the car for many years and loaned it for the Queen to use on a state visit to the Cayman Islands. The last Phantom VI was built in 1992 as a state landaulette and was to be retained by the company. However, the Sultan of Brunei was the major customer of the company at that time: He decided that he wanted the car, so off went the very last Phantom VI to join his large collection of Rolls-Royces and Bentleys.

After that car was built, production of Phantom VIs ceased, and the Hythe Road factory closed down. Corniche production had moved to Crewe, and the remaining Hythe Road workers either moved to Crewe or were laid off. The people who built the Phantom VI were wonderful coachbuilders. We saw them at work on "Lady Norfolk" and two other cars and remember their talents, the care with which they worked, their pride in the cars they built, and their great decency. With their departure went the heart of the Phantoms for a postwar world. It would be several years and the formation of a new company in a new location before we would see any new Phantoms.

A Persistent Preoccupation

Martin Cannell discusses his lifelong passion for all things Rolls-Royce and Bentley

By Craig Collins

To automotive enthusiasts and auction-house appraisers throughout Great Britain, he is known as a leading authority – quite literally "the Guru," to one auction house – on the history and culture of Rolls-Royce and the Rolls-Royce-manufactured Bentley automobiles – particularly the early postwar cars and specific categories of the collectables, such as the literature, mascots, handbooks, artwork, etc. It's probably safe to say that only a handful of people know as much as he does about the cars and the people who have built, appointed, and sold their chassis and coaches over the years. But what drives Martin Cannell of Southport, Lancashire, to collect and study all things Rolls-Royce and Bentley is, he says, simply a persistent preoccupation: "It's an overgrown hobby, really, which has often interfered with my other business interests, to say nothing of adversely affecting my golf handicap!"

Martin was launched into his lifelong obsession at a young age – he inherited it from his parents, who owned and operated a couple of local jewelry shops. "They were both very keen on motor cars," he says, "and whenever we went anywhere, whether it was down to see our family in Devon or something, every time we went past a garage, if there was an old Rolls-Royce or Bentley radiator showing in the showroom, we always seemed to stop and have a look at it."

When Martin's father bought the family's first Bentley – a secondhand Mark VI, from W. Watson & Co. Ltd. of Liverpool – in the mid-1950s, the car itself wasn't a hit in the household; his mother didn't like it because it was black. But Martin's introduction to Watson's distributorship was a revelation.

"Watson's were actually quite an interesting firm," he says, "because obviously they weren't a long, long way away from the Crewe factory. On top of that, they handled not only their own motor cars for their own distributorship, but they had a number of sub-dealers under them. And of course, in those days, a lot of the export cars going to the United States and to Australia and other places actually went from the Liverpool docks."

By his own admission, Martin spent much of his remaining youth at Watson's of Liverpool – including holidays and half-holidays from Merchant Taylors' School for Boys in nearby Crosby. He says, "Perhaps I was not the perfect pupil for a famous Public School – even though I passed the exams!"

Martin Cannell pictured after completing his Driving Test. The 1953 Bentley R Type in which he took his test was something of a surprise to the examiner.

"The Bentley was just something very, very different," he says. "They just started to fascinate me. Because my parents were so keen on cars, we used to go into so many garages and look at them. I got what books there were available on them and spent so much time in Watson's of Liverpool. I'm afraid I often used to sneak off down to Watson's when I was supposed to be doing homework and preparation for school, and I'd raid the showroom and raid the works for little

Cannell currently owns two Rolls-Royces: a rare 1951 "small-boot" Silver Dawn (above and right) and a 1957 Silver Cloud (opposite). Silver Dawns are of particular interest to Cannell.

bits of information and sales brochures, and everything else I could get my hands on, because I was fascinated by Rolls-Royce and Bentley cars. It sort of snowballed from there."

He also accompanied his father on business trips throughout Britain in order to visit other Rolls-Royce and Bentley dealers or coachbuilders. If his father drove to Yorkshire, Martin would visit the Rolls-Royce agents Hoffmann's of Halifax. If they went to a jewelry exhibition in London, he would be found at dealers such as Jack Barclay's or H.R. Owen. If they visited the south coast, he would end up in Edwards of Bournemouth. "I couldn't keep away from the damned places," he says, "and I learned so much from them over time – particularly the details of even the minor changes in the specification."

One of the first to be taken aback by Martin's encyclopedic knowledge of motor cars was his driving instructor, who, in 1960, accompanied Martin on his first and only driving lesson. His father had already been letting Martin drive around the Devon countryside for years, and the instructor thought he was a bit too precocious. "We didn't get on at all well," Martin recalls. When the day came for the Driving Test, his father said, "You can take it in the Bentley if you want to, because you've driven that more than any of them." When Martin arrived for his test in the 1953 R Type Standard Steel Sports Saloon, chassis number B.207.TO, registration number RLG 987, the examiner was shocked.

"He said, 'A Bentley!'" recalls Martin. "I said, 'Yes.' He said, 'You're actually taking your test in it?' When we got in the car, I know he was surprised – and slightly annoyed – by the car's invisible right-hand gear change, with the lever tucked to the right of the driver's seat." During the test, the examiner ordered Martin to perform a "turning in the road" – sometimes incorrectly nicknamed a three-point turn – on a narrow road. In the nearly 17-foot-long R Type, the maneuver had to become a five-point turn, but Martin didn't think he was doomed to fail the test until the examiner ordered him to perform an emergency stop. "There were no seat belts," Martin says, "and my father used to polish the seats. I mean, even my mother used to complain: 'For God's sake, Richard, why do you buff these seats so slippery? I'm sliding about.'"

Unfortunately, his father was equally finicky about the car's brakes. "Those servo brakes on Rolls and Bentleys in the 1950s, believe me, would put a lot of modern car brakes to shame," Martin says. "Of course, my dad had already said to me, 'Keep looking in your mirror, because he won't give you the emergency stop when there's a car behind you.' ... So I waited and waited. I was doing dead on 30 miles an hour when suddenly the examiner put his papers up to the windscreen and said, 'Stop!' Well, I hit those brakes, and bang! That Bentley stopped dead. I've never seen anything like it in my life. The unfortunate part of it was that the examiner went under the dashboard."

Fortunately, the examiner was a more even-tempered man than Martin had believed; at the conclusion he smiled, patted Martin on the arm, and said: "Congratulations! You've passed." Now a former official Driving Test examiner himself, Martin can strongly sympathize, retrospectively, with the poor examiner who, in 1960, drew the "short straw."

Sadly, Martin's father died at the "young" age of 67 years in 1970, but, although only in his early 20s, Martin had already bought his own first Bentley car in 1967. It was a 1947 James Young Mark VI, for which he paid £620. "I used to take my girlfriend of the time up to the Lake District in that car," he says, "but it leaked like a sieve." He soon bought another Mark VI, registration number NTU170, which he later discovered to have been an experimental model, assembled at the Crewe factory from cast-off components. The car can, in fact, be seen in Ian Rimmer's well-known book, *Rolls-Royce and Bentley Experimental Cars.*

The Mark VI and its Rolls-Royce counterpart, the Silver Dawn, have been a particular interest of Martin's; he has owned more then 25 Silver Dawns throughout his lifetime. "They have an unbelievably fascinating history, Silver Dawns, because they're much more of an important car than people have given them credit for," he says. "The Silver Dawn, in fact, is in many ways perhaps the most important Rolls-Royce of all, because it's the first Rolls-Royce car that was ever actually built by the factory. Most people don't realize that when they see all these beautiful old prewar Rolls-Royces on the road, the only thing that is Rolls-Royce about them is the chassis, the engine and the gearbox, and the back axle, because all the bodies were built by independent coachbuilders. So what you see of Rolls-Royce is actually very little; you see the radiator and the wheels, basically, and possibly the bumpers and a couple of lights."

What continues to intrigue Martin about the Silver Dawn is the Rationalized Programme decision that brought it about. Rolls-Royce was determined to produce a car that was built entirely at the Rolls-Royce factory, to avoid a dependence on dwindling coachbuilders following the introduction of mass production practices during the 1930s. "In the wartime, a prototype Standard Steel bodied car called the Ascot was built in both the Rolls-Royce and Bentley format. The decision to produce the first in-house built car as a Bentley was the result of concerns that a new Rolls-Royce model being introduced in 1946, at a time of postwar austerity, may render the very first in-house car, assembled in its entirety at the recently acquired Crewe factory, not meeting with the approval of buyers under a Labour government, and a lack of chauffeurs, etc., even though it had been designed as an 'Owner Driver' model. It was less risk to produce the

Bentley alternative, as the old firm of Bentley Motors Ltd. had only been acquired by Rolls-Royce in 1931 – and Bentley car production did not start until late 1933."

The inclusion of official orders for two coachbuilt Silver Dawns, recorded in November 1945, in the original minutes of the H.J. Mulliner board of directors company ledger, proves that the Silver Dawn had been scheduled for production long before its final introduction at the Toronto Motor Show in 1949.

Though a great collector of cars, Martin has never kept too many at one time – today he has two, a 1957 Silver Cloud, chassis number 32.B, which was the Rolls-Royce experimental car used to develop the V8 engine; and a rare 1951 "small-boot" Silver Dawn, chassis number VIN - SDB.44, registration number LYX 39, which was one of only a handful of early cars to have been registered first in the United Kingdom.

Of course, in his countless trips to designers, garages, and distributorships, he has acquired many other items of Rolls-Royce and Bentley memorabilia, including the leather Gladstone bag that Charles Rolls carried when selling the earliest Rolls-Royce cars. The bag includes a hand-stitched label inside that reads, "Dedicated to C.S. Rolls & Co., Rolls-Royce Cars, 28, Brook St., Bond St., London, W.," and is now on show, along with one of his two "Mystery" mascots, at the Rolls-Royce Enthusiasts' Club Headquarters at Paulerspury, Northamptonshire, England.

Unsurprisingly, Martin has written and published several articles about the development and history of Silver Dawns. He was also asked to write articles for "Collector's Corner" in the Rolls-Royce Enthusiasts' Club *Bulletin*, and has included features on experimental mascots and the 1910-11 sales brochure, which features the six "Arrival" pictures reproduced from the oil paintings by Charles Sykes – the creator of the Spirit of Ecstasy mascot.

In the basement of his Southport home, Martin has an immense table, nearly 4 feet across, whose top is inset with a circular slab of white and gray marble cut from the entryway floor

Cannell, pictured above with friend John Beecroft when his Bentley R Type won "Best Car in the Show" at Tatton Park, possesses a variety of Rolls-Royce and Bentley memorabilia. Currently in his collection, among numerous other items, are the original oil painting "Arrival at the Meet" by Charles Sykes (left), a leather Gladstone bag with a unique hand-stitched label that belonged to Charles Rolls (above), and a table (opposite) made with an inset of marble cut from the entryway floor of the old Rolls-Royce showroom on London's Conduit Street.

of the old Rolls-Royce showroom in Conduit Street in London. The marble is inscribed with Charles Sykes' Spirit of Ecstasy design, and above the figure appears the date "1929" – believed to be the year that the Conduit Street showrooms were refurbished and also the year that the company celebrated the Silver Jubilee of the meeting of F.H. Royce and C.S. Rolls after their partnership meeting at the Midland Hotel in Manchester, England, in 1904.

Martin also owns two important original oil paintings by Charles Sykes, "Arrival at the Meet" – one of six Sykes was commissioned to paint for Rolls-Royce's 1910-11 sales brochure – and "A Ghost Overtaken by the Dawn," which hung in the Conduit Street office of Rolls-Royce throughout the early 20th century.

Though he's never counted the items in his collection, Martin estimates that they number in the thousands – items as varied as owner handbooks, including Charles Rolls' own; countless sales brochures, including three variants of the 1910-11 sales catalogue; a ledger of the minutes of meetings held at famed coachbuilder H.J. Mulliner from 1910 to 1959; and one of the 1951 Clan Foundry portfolios for the Rolls-Royce "Corniche II," precursor to the Bentley Continental, designed at the experimental "Clan Foundry" in Belper, Derbyshire, which may well be the only one in private hands.

Two of the items in his collection, experimental mascots designed by Charles Sykes as an alternative to the Spirit of Ecstasy, received much attention in 2003, when several friends alerted Martin to an article in *The Daily Telegraph* about a unique Sykes-designed mascot, reportedly the only one of its kind, featuring a lady with a sweeping hood behind her head.

Martin already had two of these "one-of-a-kind" mascots, which he had acquired earlier from an elderly former employee of the Park, Ward coachbuilders company who had retired at the time of the Rolls-Royce Limited takeover in 1939. The Park, Ward personnel had been using the "Hood" – a water-collecting feature that likely doomed the mascot from being mounted atop the radiator cap – as an ashtray. "They were absolutely filthy," Martin says. He left them in a box for some time before taking them out, cleaning them up, and discovering, on the back of the lady's veil, the signature of Charles Sykes. Excited, Martin tried to contact the original owner in Surrey, but so many years had passed that he was unable to locate him.

Of the "Mystery Mascots," as Martin has dubbed them, there are now four known – two of which belong to him. It's not yet clear to anyone which car they were originally designed to adorn, but it may well have been for the 20 h.p. cars introduced in 1922, as this was the date the family involved in the first article about these items had been given the piece – reportedly by Charles Sykes himself. The first one of these mascots to be offered for sale by Bonhams was sold in the United States for approximately US$27,000, including buyer's premium.

Martin has acquired so much memorabilia over the years that he's now of a mind to winnow things a bit. "Some of the sales brochures I've got in duplicate, triplicate, even quadruplicate. So I'm trying to get rid of the surplus." While he will retain his most treasured items – such as the Sykes paintings, the Mystery Mascots, the "Horizontal Wing" mascot from a New Phantom experimental car, the 1st Edition Handbook from Charles Rolls' Gladstone bag, and the marble table fashioned from a piece of the Conduit Street showroom's floor – he

has recently put many of his brochures and handbooks up for auction.

Nevertheless, his passion for all things Rolls-Royce and Bentley remains. He's put his experimental Silver Cloud on the market and is on the lookout for a Bentley, possibly an S Type Continental by Mulliner. "I wouldn't mind, just for a change, even possibly a prewar car, although I don't like driving them as much as the postwar ones," he says. "I've also got the potential offer of a Mark VI Bentley Drophead."

A self-described "staid old Briton," Martin – while he loves to drive his Rolls-Royce cars – doesn't take them out of the U.K. "I go up to the Lake District regularly, as well as down south to Devon and to numerous RREC

Rallies and Classic Car events," he says. "The Silver Cloud has been up and down to the Lake District more times than I care to remember. On summer evenings, I'll often take one of my cars out. My lady friend and I will have a go round up into nice parts of Lancashire and places like that, and have a pie and a pint."

Though Martin loves Rolls-Royce and Bentley cars fiercely, and drives them regularly, he doesn't see the point of hoarding them – he prefers to own them one or two at a time. "I'll probably just keep turning them over and have another change – buy one, sell one, maybe when I want to change it," he says. "For what I do, I really only need one, or perhaps two, in case one 'fails to proceed' – which of course would never happen!"

This photo: 1970, Blenheim prize-giving and M.R. Neale's 1912 40/50 hp Hamshaw tourer, 2087E. Clothes were still conventional, but now with the occasional pair of corduroy jeans. **Opposite:** 1965, Blenheim. Phil Duce's 1933 Phantom II James Young four-door tourer. Roland Duce, still at school, was then affecting a hairstyle somewhere between DA and Mod.

Every Picture Tells a Story

By Colin Hughes

Looking back at the photographs he has generated over his years of attending Rolls-Royce Enthusiasts' Club (RREC) rallies since the late 1950s, the author finds himself struck by the way that the clothes, hairstyles, hats, handbags, even picnic gear, now give the scenes a period look.

Above, left: 1966, Blenheim. Miss Mary Wentworth Kelly with her 1961 Silver Cloud II H.J. Mulliner drophead coupé, SXC637. She always hired a chauffeur for these rallies for the obvious reason you can see.
Above, right: 1960, at Bolney. Stanley Sears with his 1912 40/50 hp Hooper limousine, 1721, one of the first early Rolls-Royce cars to be restored. **Left:** 1970, Vichy Tour. Bill Meredith-Owens and Stuart Fortune examine a 1913 40/50 hp, 2534. Abroad, British summer clothing was still shirtsleeves, but with hats that might not be risked at home.

A t the time I took the photographs or shot the movies, people were part of the clutter that interfered with my aim of getting a replica of a coachbuilder's photograph of a car as when new. If I achieved that aim, I had a picture that gave no sense of when it was taken. The passage of time has made me regret this.

Few of us are sensitive at the time that our clothes may reflect their period when observed from even only 10 years hence. I first became aware of this from cine film footage I shot in the 1960s, where the presence of people passing through the scenes was part of the ambience.

Most of us can tell relatively quickly when a film of a period drama was set by looking at the clothes and hairstyles of the characters. Moreover, even people outside the old car world can tell the era of an old car. One of the games Mermie Karger and I played when crossing the United

Above, left: 1977, Packington. Getting ready to watch the prize-giving: Notice the wide lapels, safari jackets, flared trousers, and the kids' hairstyles. **Above, right:** 1976, Stowe. Eustace Hope, Ron Haynes, John Fasal, and Trevor Glenroy examining Eustace's 1927 20 hp, GHJ66. Note the hairstyles and the advent of jeans.
Right: 1978, Yarnton. Picnics were still at ground level on a dry day. Graham Neale's 1911 40/50 hp two-seater in the style of Rippon 1557 and J. Wright's 20 hp Park Ward doctor's coupé, GEN78.

States recently in her 1938 Phantom III, when asked the age of the car, was to suggest people guess. A few were over 10 years wrong either way, but many were within three or so years, based on the style of the body. The pictures in this article are mainly for looking at people – the cars are incidental.

Following World War II until the mid-1950s, new cars in the U.K. were on allocation: You might have to wait a year for delivery, so many prewar cars were still in everyday use. If you

Above: 2010, Rockingham. Will Fiennes driving R. Raynsford's 1932 20/25 hp Graber drophead coupé, GRW59, at the prize-giving. Will today's fashions stand the test of time? **Left:** 2010, Rockingham. Judging D. Webster's 1935 3½-Litre Park Ward drophead coupé, B25CW. In 10 or 20 years' time, what will this kid think of what he was wearing?

had only just started a job, new cars were out of the question anyway. In an unheated car, one's clothing might include a British Warm ex-military service overcoat, or a naval surplus duffel coat. Since central heating was in the minority in U.K. homes, most of us wore heavy pullovers even indoors. Fashion didn't come into it: Comfort was the aim.

At the time the first RREC Concours d'Elegance was run in 1959, many of the cars that turned up were either recently acquired by people of limited means who used them every day, or had been in the family since nearly new. At that time, one either wore a suit, or in really cold weather or in an open car, you might wear an overcoat of up to 24-ounce cloth, while if the sun came

out, you would go around in shirtsleeves, occasionally even removing your tie.

When my brother, Nigel, and I first went to RREC events and worked on the various Rolls-Royce wrecks on Eddie Harris' farm at Yarnton near Oxford, we just wore our ordinary clothes. At that time, as university students, we generally wore sports jackets and flannel trousers: none of today's T-shirts and jeans for us then, nor any protective clothing to satisfy the needs of health and safety. Rolling up one's shirtsleeves to avoid getting too much grease on them was about as far as one went.

During the 1960s, old cars started to develop a following; there were relatively well-off people in their 20s who would buy Rolls-Royce 20/25s that had been pulled out of barns or acquired from car hire and funeral firms by the dealers who lurked in various Mews garages in London, Kensington in particular. The dealers gave the predominantly black cars a quick blow-over with bright coloured body sides, and after minor dent removal from the mudguards, some more black paint, usually visible as overspray on the mud beneath. New rubber-backed carpet from Cyril Lord ("Carpet you can afford") and possibly a new headliner, if the moths had been active, completed the

2009, Kelmarsh Hall. D. Williams' 1928 40/65 hp New Phantom Murphy cabriolet, S342FM, and the rise of the baseball cap.

deal. A £100 car would become a £500 one for the expenditure of £200. Probably an oil and coolant change might be all else that the car had received.

These newly made-over Rolls-Royces were popular for doing the evening drag up the King's Road in Chelsea. The owners might affect the 1930s dress of boating blazer and straw hat, though white trousers were probably a mistake with the way cars oozed oil and especially if the dealer had treated the leather with "Tuxan," a staining restorer that could come off on clothing: not popular with the girlfriend.

Toward the end of the 1960s, the old car movement was becoming more widespread and the sort of people at Rolls-Royce rallies became much as they are today, with a gradual increase in members with the more modern cars. The pictures here, covering the period from around 1960 to the end of the 1970s, depict the situation that has continued: older people dress traditionally, the young more *au courant*. Children's clothing, too. Look at trends in hair and skirt length, as well.

A few pictures taken fairly recently are included for you to ponder when you fish out this yearbook in 10 or more years' time.

Many of the people appearing in the older photographs are no longer with us: Where anyone is mentioned in captions, please recognize that I am observing their style, not criticizing it. I hope that those of you who see yourselves when rather younger will view the pictures with nostalgia and amusement.

I R O N I E S

Los Angeles
San Francisco
New York
Chicago
Denver
Seattle
Houston
Dallas
DCOTA
Atlanta
Boston
510.644.2100
WWW.IRONIÉS.COM

The Father of the Modern Rolls-Royce

By David Evans

History is replete with occasions where mild-mannered, retiring individuals come briefly onto a stage, play a significant role, and then retire once more into the shadows. The history of Rolls-Royce is no exception.

T he company's history includes many individuals who have performed a similar role, but in the last half-century of the history of Rolls-Royce, there is one individual who, through his foresight and determination, stands out from the rest in that he laid the groundwork for the success of Rolls-Royce PLC today and who can truly be called "the Father of the modern Rolls-Royce motor car." That individual is Edward Rupert Nicholson, a pipe-smoking, quietly spoken accountant from Surrey, England. For his actions as receiver of Rolls-Royce Limited in 1971, he was spurned by the Heath government and the establishment never forgave him for his opposition to their wishes.

What led such a quiet, unassuming man to this uncomfortable position? Rolls-Royce Ltd. had, since the mid-1960s, been involved in the RB211 engine project. With considerable financial support of the then U.K. government under Harold Wilson, the company had commenced development of the engine in the late 1960s and had concluded an agreement with Lockheed to supply the new engine for installation in their TriStar aircraft. The government had underwritten the contract in terms of the development and performance of the engine. With the change of government in 1970, the new administration was not empathetic to the massive state funding of industrial projects in the manner of their predecessors and they attempted to reduce the level of that support wherever possible.

Opposite: Rupert Nicholson in his library. This page: Then-British Prime Minister Harold Wilson (above, left) had given considerable support to the development of the RB211 engine and finalized the agreement to supply it for the Lockheed TriStar (right), but his successor, Edward Heath (above, right), was anxious to distance his administration from the commitment.

The RB211 engine represented a major technical advance over engines currently in use at that time in that it was a three-shaft engine as opposed to the two-shaft engines that were the standard of the time. This design promised improved performance and, in particular, improved power-to-weight ratio. Furthermore, the design was modular, which made servicing of the engine much less expensive, since many modules could be replaced in the field without a complete engine change. The contract with Lockheed required that the new engine reach certain performance levels and in view of the complexity of the new design, Rolls-Royce was having technical difficulties in achieving these performance targets.

By the new year of 1971, the major problems with this development were becoming apparent and it was consuming funds at a rapid rate while the eventual sales were being further delayed, leaving the company with an increasing funding gap. Although Rolls-Royce had been able to raise additional funds from its bankers and had also received support from the U.K. government, by January 1971, it was quite clear that Rolls-Royce's liabilities were large and of indeterminate extent. The Heath government was particularly concerned at the open-ended commitment of the contract with Lockheed and were anxious to repudiate it. As January moved into February, Rolls-Royce's bankers became more concerned and reduced its overdraft facilities from £50 million to £40 million while, at the same time, the future cash flow requirement for continuing to fund the RB211 project was expanding rapidly. It was crystal clear that Rolls-Royce was technically insolvent. The government said it would do nothing more; as a result, on February 4, 1971, Nicholson was appointed receiver.

Edward Rupert Nicholson was born in Southsea, Hampshire, on September 17, 1909, the eldest of three boys and three girls. The family moved to the Home Counties, where he attended Whitgift School in Croydon, Surrey. He was a keen sportsman; he played rugby on the wing for the old Whitgiftian's first XV and was also a keen cricketer and had a keen and incisive mind that made him a formidable opponent at bridge. On leaving school, Nicholson took articles in his father's firm of chartered accountants and after qualification, in the mid-'30s, he moved to Peat Marwick Mitchell & Company (now part of KPMG); it was here he began to develop his skills in receivership work.

The new receiver was called upon to take some fairly momentous decisions very quickly after his appointment. At 8 a.m. on the first day of the announcement, the gates of the Rolls-Royce factories had been shut with the best intentions of protecting the interests of the shareholders of the existing company, but with unfortunate consequences. The situation was so dire that a chauffeur arriving at Crewe with his employer to collect his new Rolls-Royce motor car on February 3 had left it in the factory overnight. When the

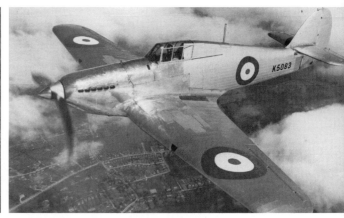

The huge contribution that aircraft such as the Hurricane (left) and the Lancaster (right) made during World War II was still fresh in the public's mind.

Top: The headlines following Rolls-Royce's bankruptcy in 1971.
Left: Charles Rolls. **Right:** Henry Royce.

chauffeur returned at 8 a.m. on February 4, he was told that his employer would have to pay for the car again if he still wanted it! Nicholson was told of this and immediately gave unconditional clearance for the unfortunate chauffeur to collect the car, since he realized that if he was to preserve the goodwill of Rolls-Royce, he needed to make sure that such legalistic maneuvers were avoided at all costs. As that grim day wore on, Nicholson gave a brief statement to the media to the effect that it was his intention to endeavor to save Rolls-Royce – a statement which Nicholson himself later admitted was an act of blind faith but which, nevertheless, was much appreciated by the employees of the company.

Meanwhile, the effect on the U.K. public was almost the same as if the nation itself had gone into receivership. Rolls-Royce Ltd. was the premier engineering company in the kingdom; it had designed and built the engines which had been so successful in both the First and the Second World Wars. In the minds of the public in 1971, the memories of the Second World War were still raw and the achievements of aircraft such as the Spitfire, Hurricane, Mosquito, Lancaster, and the Mustang were all still relatively fresh in people's minds. Surely, Rolls-Royce can't go bust – the government wouldn't allow it, would they? Conspiracy theories abounded – some within the company thought that the government had delib-

erately engineered insolvency since the government wished to extricate themselves from the potential liabilities under the contract with Lockheed.

Rupert Nicholson had other ideas – he had the foresight and the imagination to realize that the RB211 engine was not only a major step forward in the field but was, in fact, a potential world-beater and the start of a completely new generation of aero-engines. He knew that the company had all the necessary intellectual property rights to the design and that, if successful, this family of engines would dominate aeronautics for decades to come. He also realized the value of the name. He understood that the Rolls-Royce name had significant value in its own right. As time moved on from the commencement of receivership, Nicholson worked tirelessly to further the interests of the company and its products.

Meanwhile, in the outside world, interested parties and potential competitors were lining up to pick over the entrails of the company. The U.K. government was intent on obtaining as much short-term cash back for the taxpayers as it possibly could, without any thought for the future – a future which, for Rolls-Royce, looked very bleak indeed.

On the day after his appointment, Nicholson was called to a meeting with Lord Carrington, who was Minister for Aviation. Carrington was insistent that the first order of

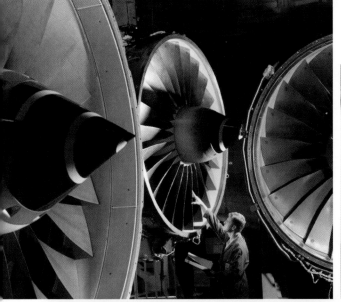

Lord Carrington (left) was initially insistent that the Lockheed contract should be repudiated, but gradually realized the potential of the RB211 (far left). **Bottom:** Nicholson showed his mettle a few days after his appointment as receiver by allowing the launch of the Corniche.

of faith in the circumstances and for which Carrington deserves considerable credit.

There then remained the problem as to what to do with the motor cars. In 1971, this was a separate division within Rolls-Royce Ltd. based at its own factory environment at Crewe. The division at that time was partly funded by its ability to supply components to the aero-engine divisions at Derby and elsewhere around the country, but nevertheless it was a separate entity that could be packaged up and sold on. The world's motor manufacturers were waiting in the wings to snap up such a valuable prize. Nicholson, however, would have none of it – he needed to raise all the money he could for the benefit of the creditors and the shareholders of Rolls-Royce Limited, and to do that, he needed to retain the association of the name Rolls-Royce with the cars. So instead of doing as the government wished and float the motor division as "Bentley," he resisted, formed Rolls-Royce Motor Cars Ltd., and allowed the company to continue trading. It was a measure of Nicholson's determination that he allowed the launch of the "Corniche" to go ahead just a few days after his appointment as receiver of the company.

Thus was born Rolls-Royce Motor Cars Ltd. as the Crewe operation became, and it continued in business until December 31, 2002. To protect the motor car business, Nicholson arranged for the grant of an exclusive licence to Rolls-Royce Motor Cars Ltd. from Rolls-Royce (1971) Ltd. in perpetuity and at no cost. The licence provided for Rolls-Royce Motor Cars Ltd. to use the trademarks in respect of its automotive products and also, incidentally, in respect of model motor cars. The licence provided, however, that in the event that the company became foreign owned, the licence would terminate within 28 days and the name would revert to the aero-engine company. The effect of the grant of this license was to increase the attractiveness of the

business for Nicholson was the repudiation of the Lockheed contract and the second order of business was to ensure preservation of the capability of any nationalized entity to service the various ongoing defense contracts. Nicholson realized that if he did this, Rolls-Royce in the future, in whatever guise it survived, would be finished as a major player in the aeronautical field. His solution was to retain the money that the U.K. government had already put into Rolls-Royce Ltd. and to restructure the company while at the same time renegotiating the financial arrangements for the Lockheed contract. Over a remarkably short period

of time, Nicholson's team managed to achieve this feat and the concept behind Rolls-Royce (1971) Ltd., the nationalized company, was born. He took the bold stroke of valuing the RB211 Engine project at £1 thus at a stroke, wiping out the huge investment that the U.K. government had in the project! The Heath government was furious at this apparent disregard for the taxpayers' interests. But within the government one man was having a change of heart: Carrington began to realize the potential of the engine and he continued to support the company under the terms of the Indemnity Agreement with Lockheed, which was a huge act

MODULINE®
MODULAR ALUMINUM CABINETS

"Organizing with Style" is as easy as 1-2-3 with Moduline's modular all aluminum garage cabinets. Designed and manufactured in the USA since 1988 by a team steeped in automotive shop design and race car support, their focus is on balancing function vs. beauty. The result is utilitarian as well as eye catching and fashionable; perfect for creating that special look in your garage or automotive themed room that will look attractive for a lifetime.

The high gloss enamel finished panels, surrounded by anodized and sealed "brushed aluminum" frames, create a stunning and lasting impression on everyone. Durable and engineered to last a lifetime, standard features include rugged full frame cabinet design, full extension ball bearing drawer slides, lockable tool chests and double walled inner hat braced cabinet doors with full length hinges.

Each customer is assigned a personal member of the Moduline Team to help guide them through the overall design and selection process. With a variety of standard modular cabinets and tool chests to choose from, when they arrive and are installed, they will look as if they were custom designed and fabricated just for your particular home.

Manufactured using only the highest quality materials available, each unit is fully assembled and inspected at our factory prior to shipment assuring the highest levels of customer satisfaction.

Found in many automotive enthusiasts' residences, individuals particular about their garage choose Moduline cabinetry and tool storage products.

1-888-343-4463
www.modulinegarage.com

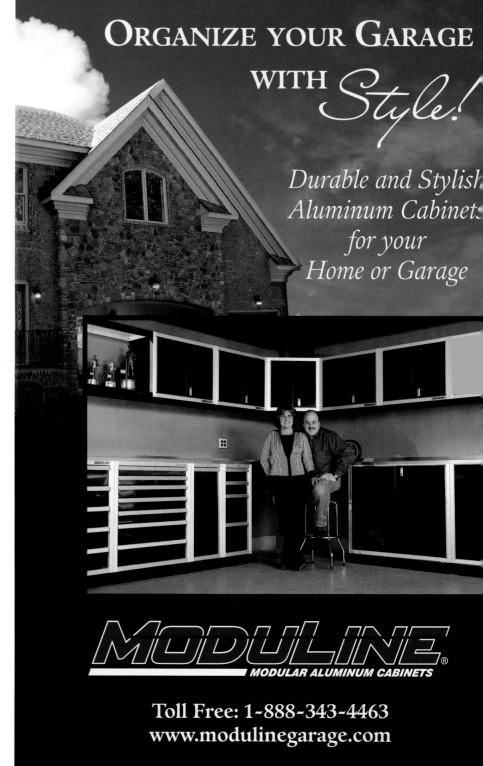

Top: The Rolls-Royce tradition lives on at the Goodwood head office. **Middle left:** The manufacturing facility where the Phantom (middle right and bottom) is built.

newly formed Rolls-Royce Motor Cars Ltd. to potential investors so that when it was eventually floated on the market in 1973, Nicholson managed to receive some £37.2 million, which went into the liquidation accounts to benefit the creditors and the shareholders of the old company.

At the end of the receivership, all the creditors were paid in full and the shareholders received a significant return. When challenged in later years that the company was not really insolvent because of the eventual outcome and the suggestion that the whole exercise had been a plot by the government to extricate itself from potential liability under the Lockheed contract, Nicholson pointed out that in 1971, Rolls-Royce Ltd. was hopelessly bankrupt; creditors were being held off and they doubted their ability even to pay the next week's wages!

For his stout resistance to the Heath government, the establishment never forgave him and Nicholson never received the knighthood that many thought he so richly deserved. What he did in those few short years was to encourage and promote the development of an aero-engine that subsequently transmogrified into the Trent family of engines that we have today and which at the time of writing is fitted to some 56 percent of all large capacity commercial aircraft manufactured worldwide.

More than that, however, Nicholson ensured that the Rolls-Royce motor car would continue with its own independent heritage. We all know the story of the sale of Rolls-Royce Motor Cars by Vickers in 1998 and the insistence by Rolls-Royce PLC that BMW should continue with the motor car tradition. It was Nicholson who had insisted on the reversion clause in the licence agreement, and by doing so, he prevented the name from being simply subsumed as a badge variant in the Volkswagen empire. Nicholson had insisted that Rolls-Royce should remain British and when the deal with BMW was struck 27 years later, Rolls-Royce PLC insisted that the new Rolls-Royce motor cars were to be built in England. As a result, the Rolls-Royce tradition in motor cars lives on; the new Phantom is built at Goodwood in Sussex, England, and was consciously designed in the tradition of a long line of Rolls-Royce motor cars. BMW has followed faithfully that dictum of Henry Royce that we should take the best that exists, improve it, and use it.

None of this would have been possible without the stand that Rupert Nicholson took in 1971/2 against the British government in maintaining the integrity of the company of which he was receiver to ensure that it lived on, while at the same time floating off the motor company in a manner that ensured that he obtained the maximum price for the assets while the name and tradition remained British. Without Nicholson, the wonderful selection of post-1971 Rolls-Royce motor cars simply would not exist.

We owe a huge debt to Edward Rupert Nicholson and, in the writer's mind, he truly is "the Father of the Modern Rolls-Royce."

The Breitling GMT Chronograph.

Time Machines for Time Machines

Bentley and Breitling deliver
extreme performance and style

By Jan Tegler

In the broadest sense, automobiles and watches are time machines:
The watch measures time while the automobile compresses time,
shortening the duration of land-based journeys. At their best, both
combine elements of performance, style, and heritage, which make
them timely and timeless.

Consider the latest releases from Bentley and Breitling. The Continental Supersports debuted in early 2010, setting a new standard of performance for the marque – the fastest model ever to issue from the crew
at Crewe. This extreme Bentley can sprint from zero to 60 mph in just
3.7 seconds, reach a top speed of 204 mph, and crack off lighting-quick
shifts in just 200 milliseconds. How's that for a time machine?

Breitling's new Bentley Supersports Chronograph is a fitting
complement to the supercar. Designed to evoke the Supersports,
the limited-edition Supersports Chronograph takes styling cues
from the British-built rocket's interior and turns in its own impressive performance. Equipped with a self-winding, high-frequency

movement beating at 28,800 vibrations per hour, the Swiss-made chrono can measure time to the quarter-second, track elapsed time to the 12-hour mark, and calculate average speed via its world-exclusive "variable tachometer" with circular slide rule. It's a superchronograph for a supercar.

Then there's the 2011 Continental GT, a new version of the popular model that has been in production for seven years. An undeniable hit, 23,000 examples of the GT have been built to date. The second generation of the powerful coupe and convertible updates the big two-door with sportier styling, a choice of power plants, and more driver-focused appeal than ever. It's a world beating time machine that can burn up the road with even greater speed and sophistication than its predecessor.

To do it justice, Breitling has created a limited edition world-timer, an exclusive version of its Bentley GMT Chronograph. Trimmed in British Racing Green and featuring a clever multiple time zone display, the GMT exudes the modern yet classic panache of the new Continental GT.

Driving and wearing these time machines is the surest way to appreciate their respective quality, so we paired them side by side for a closer look.

BENTLEY CONTINENTAL SUPERSPORTS AND BREITLING SUPERSPORTS CHRONOGRAPH

If the current Continental GT looks large-and-in-charge, the Supersports looks like the boss – more muscular, more aggressive, more commanding. Lowered by 0.4 inches, the Supersports is wider than the standard GT, its rear track stretched by 2 inches with brawny fender flares covering 20-inch forged alloy wheels.

Direct your eyes to the front end of the car: It stares back at you more purposefully. Larger air intakes carved into its face channel additional airflow to the Supersports' intercoolers and radiators, providing a charge of cooled air that boosts the output of the model's massive 6-liter, twin-turbocharged W12 engine. The vents also send air to cool the extreme Bentley's huge carbon ceramic disc brakes, create additional downforce over the car's front axle to bolster grip, and extract heat from the engine bay.

The Bentley Continental Supersports, lighter than the current Continental GT, boasts increased performance and can race from zero to 60 in 3.7 seconds.

Brightwork normally found on the radiator grille, bonnet vents, vertical intakes, and headlight bezels is transformed with a smoked steel finish. The wheels are similarly dark, lending the entire package a serious bearing no matter which of the available 27 exterior colors you choose.

That's as it should be considering the legacy behind the "Supersports" moniker. The original Supersports debuted in 1925 as a limited edition, race-bred, short-wheelbase version of the legendary "Speed 3" 3-Litre. Motivated by an overhead-cam inline four cylinder, the two-seater put out a whopping 85 hp, good enough to push the car to approximately 100 mph. Thus Bentley laid claim to the first production car to achieve three-digit speed. The Supersports won further glory with a triumph at the 24 Hours of Le Mans in 1927.

The modern Supersports' Bentley DNA doesn't end there. Exterior styling was influenced by the stunning R-type

While the interior of the Supersports includes less traditional materials – carbon fiber stands in for wood – the Breitling clock, standard in all Bentley models, remains.

Continental, which launched in 1952 as the fastest four-seater in the world. Today's Supersports echoes the long bonnet, sleek cabin, and burly rear fenders seen on the R-type. The model also builds on the spirit of the Bentley Speed 8 Le Mans prototypes, which scored a one-two finish at Le Mans in 2003.

The proof is in the drive. Put your foot to the floor in the Supersports and you'll gather up the horizon before you know it. With 621 hp and a road-rippling 590 pound-feet of torque on hand, the coupe leaps to 60 mph in 3.7 seconds, followed just two-tenths later by the convertible version. The quarter mile passes by in about 12 seconds. By that time you're closing on 120 mph, still a little more than 80 mph shy of terminal velocity.

At some point (probably very soon on American roads), you'll need to do away with all that speed. Fortunately, it's a simple proposition thanks to the impossibly huge 16.5-inch front/13-inch rear binders fitted to the Supersports. Mash the brake pedal and nearly 5,000 pounds of luxury sedan comes to a halt quicker than you can say "carbon-ceramic!"

The 40/60 torque split of the Supersports' continuous all-wheel-drive system combined with its independent suspension (with adjustable dampers) and battleship-solid chassis endows the big coupe with unexpected agility. You'd never guess it could dance the way it does over back roads, only breaking traction if you do something really, really ill-advised.

The Supersports' ability to generate pace effortlessly is aided by its seamless ZF six-speed transmission. Shifts come creamy smooth, one after another. If you prefer to choose gears yourself, steering wheel-mounted paddles allow you to dictate shifts, although the stalk-type paddles (the same as in lesser Continentals) are not ideal for the task.

But the exterior and performance of this extreme Bentley are only half the story. Inside, the Supersports sets itself apart from other Continentals in many ways, including some that contribute to the supercar's super-quickness.

"Our main focus with the interior was to take weight out of the car," says Robin Page, Bentley's head of Interior Design. "That was another opportunity to increase the performance of the car compared to the current GT. The first element we focused on was introducing carbon-fiber seats. Straightaway that took out a substantial amount of weight [90 pounds]. We also took the opportunity to move the mounting location of the seatbelts from the seats themselves to what we call the rear-quarter, which is part of the main structure of the chassis. That enabled us to reduce weight further. We did all that on the initial Supersports, the two-seater. Taking the rear seats out saved even more weight."

Sporting as it is, the Supersports' cabin doesn't sacrifice luxury. Customers can also choose softer, more conventional seats in a four-seat configuration with the added advantage of greater adjustment (the carbon-fiber chairs are limited in height adjustment). Cast alloy foot pedals with rubber grips meet the driver's feet in just the right spot.

Look further around the interior and you'll notice other cues that set the Supersports apart. Seat and door colors are more extroverted,

The Breitling Supersports Chronograph.

highlighted with contrasting piping and stitching. Alcantara® makes its first appearance in a Bentley while carbon fiber replaces traditional wood accents to make a modern statement.

"Once we achieved our first objective, we started to play around with the trim," Page affirms. "We used Alcantara to get a grippier material for the seats and also sportier diamond-flute stitching that harkens back to our heritage and is a very sporting graphic. We put that diamond quilting into the doors and into the rear compartment. There is carbon fiber on the fascia and the console."

It is in the instrument cluster that the intersection between the Supersports and Supersports Chronograph comes to the fore. Beyond the Breitling clock found on the upper console (standard in all Bentley models), the new graphics found on the Supersports' gauges are also evident on the dashboard-style dial of the chronograph. Red accents on the chrono's hands and totalizers evoke the indicators on the car's speedometer, tachometer, and water temperature and fuel gauges.

Run a finger over the Supersports Chronograph's bezel and you'll find the same raised, knurled texture evident on the car's shift knob and switches, providing a tactile connection between watch and auto. A cambered, glare-proofed sapphire crystal gives the dial easy legibility in any light while a titanium caseback provides strength and helps keep down the weight of the watch's large, handsome, 48.7-millimeter case.

Under the chronograph's elegant Royal Ebony dial is a power plant worthy of the Supersports. Breitling's automatic Calibre 26B certified chronometer movement operates as flawlessly and smoothly as the Bentley's drivetrain. A satisfying click of the Supersports Chronograph's pushers immediately starts and stops its 12-hour and 60-minute counters while the central scale provides hundredth-of-an-hour and hundredth-of-a-minute accuracy. The model's variable tachometer – contrary to common tachometers that cannot extend beyond 60-second

The 2011 Bentley Continental GT gets a boost in power – 575 hp up from 560 hp – as well as a boost in technology: The interior features a touch screen that controls the audio and navigation systems, the phone, and the comfort settings.

periods – serves to measure average speed whatever the time elapsed, the distance covered, or the speed reached.

Available in just 1,000 pieces with rubber strap or Speed bracelet, the Supersports Chronograph is the perfect accessory for the Supersports. Strap into this supercar, strap on the super-chronograph, and blast off!

2011 BENTLEY CONTINENTAL AND BREITLING GMT CHRONOGRAPH

The "Winged Bs" of Bentley and Breitling cross paths once more in the new Continental GT and GMT Chronograph. The latest in the Breitling-for-Bentley line is perfect for pairing with the modern revision of the now-classic GT.

On sale in 2011, the updated GT features a revised body. Its grille and hood are drawn back and lower, increasing aerodynamic efficiency and emphasizing power bulges and character lines

You've come to expect a certain level of comfort in your life. But this – this is beyond what you anticipated: A hotel, in the heart of the nation's capital, that feels like an extension of your own home. Where you are greeted warmly by name on arrival. Where the door opens on your impeccably styled suite to reveal the ambience and scale of a private Parisian salon. Where dining tables – among the most sought-after in the city – are tucked into quiet corners to invite relaxed conversation as you savor the award-winning flavors of Plume. And where an intimate spa can, depending on your inclination, deliver a classic close shave or Crushed Cabernet Celestial Sugar Glow.

Washington's movers and shakers and the world's elite have long felt at home at The Jefferson, drawn to our prestigious address and reputation for discretion. Now, our Beaux Arts gem is completely transformed. Every aspect of your stay is elevated, inspired by the personal passions of our namesake, Thomas Jefferson, the consummate Renaissance man who for eight years held court at the White House just four blocks south.

Every turn holds a new delight. Just beyond the lobby, sunlight once again streams through a magnificent 1923 skylight, rediscovered after decades under wraps. In the Private Cellar, a dumbwaiter fashioned after Jefferson's own at Monticello conveys your choice of vintage from a carefully curated list of more than 6,000 fine and rare bottles. In the fire-warmed Book Room, walls lined with beautifully bound Jeffersonian tomes encourage you to settle in for an after-dinner read and cognac. From your suite, a simple button just inside the door produces a subtle hallway light to convey to housekeeping your wishes for service or privacy.

This is grandeur on an intimate scale. This is Washington's finest small hotel. This is The Jefferson, Washington, DC. And you hold the key.

THE JEFFERSON
WASHINGTON DC

1200 16th Street NW Washington, DC 20036
t:202.448.2300 · f:202.448.2301 | WWW.JEFFERSONDC.COM

over the front wheels. The cabin's greenhouse extends into a shorter rear deck while newly styled wheels and subtly altered tail lamps further distinguish the new car.

The underpinnings of the coupe and convertible remain largely unchanged but under the bonnet there's news. The GT's twin-turbo W12 gets a boost in power, up from 560 hp to 575 hp, and torque jumping from 479 pound-feet to 516. What's more, there's a new option for power. In 2012, Bentley will offer the GT with the familiar W12 or a 4.0-liter V8. The all-new engine, developed in partnership with Audi, will be more fuel efficient and produce lower emissions. Output is expected to be in the 350 hp to 400 hp range.

Taking its cue from the Supersports, the new GT's continuous all-wheel-drive achieves a 40/60 front/rear torque split. And last but not least, the Continental GT goes on a diet, losing 143 pounds from its curb weight. That weight savings can again be attributed to Bentley's interior design team led by Page and their work to lighten the two-door's seats and interior components.

Three priorities guided the team's work, says Page.

"First, we wanted to make the interior lighter, sportier, and more dynamic. We took inspiration from an athlete who had been on a training program and looked at muscle tone. You'll see that the design of the car is more modern and we used very strong graphics to give a dynamic feel to the interior.

"We put a very soft foam frame under the leather of the new seats," he continues. "It's really difficult to do this because you have to develop a substructure very carefully to make sure you keep a nice sharp modern design language on the surfaces of the seats. Everywhere you touch the leather, it's soft. We learned this trick by using it in the Mulsanne. The old Continental GT doesn't feel as luxurious as the new Mulsanne. The foam allows the leather to stay very soft."

The second stage involved talking to the brand's customers about technology, Page reveals.

"We took a step forward. In our entertainment system, which includes navigation, climate control, and more, we've now got a touch screen. In that touch screen you can use the latest three-dimensional graphics. We've got a 30-gigabyte memory in there and really, the latest technology available. Our customers expect the latest updates – Google mapping and to be able to load 15 gigabytes of music, and the three-dimensional mapping so when you go into a city you can see the buildings rising out of the map. We've also introduced a digital version of the knurled texture we have on our physical switches to the touch screen display. So there's a bit of Bentley going into the technology as well, a bit of tradition."

Third, the interior design team added space to the cabin both in terms of stowage and rear-seat legroom. There's an additional 46 millimeters between rear passenger's knees and the front seatbacks and more room for stowage in door pockets. The team also included a clever, removable glass case, finished in wood trim matching the dash and console.

Driver awareness has been enhanced by a display placed between the speedometer and tachometer, which shows premium information including vehicle systems cues and a range of other data. Again, Bentley and Breitling worked together to harmonize the look of the gauges in the GT's instrument cluster, its integral Breitling clock, and the limited-edition GMT Chronograph.

"We invite Breitling over [to Crewe] at the start of projects," says Page. "They come see the first styling model of a new car. We talk about the design language of the exterior and interior

The design teams of Bentley and Breitling meet at the start of projects to discuss the styling and materials (both interior and exterior) of a new car model. Breitling then incorporates those details into its timepieces.

and the materials and details. From that, they try to pick up themes they can incorporate into their ongoing designs. Obviously, their design program is shorter than ours, so they get a look at what we're doing and then think about new designs. We get together with them again as the design process advances. It's a nice working relationship."

This time around, the result is the GMT Chronograph. Only 1,000 examples will be produced, highlighted by a special British Racing Green inner bezel and rubber strap. The chrono's dial graphics mirror those in the new Continental GT, ringed by a 24-city time zone scale. A second 24-hour time zone is adjustable via a pushpiece integrated into the left side of the attention-getting 49 millimeter steel case.

Breitling's automatic, self-winding Caliber 47B certified chronometer movement functions as fluidly as the GT, featuring a one-eighth of a second chronograph, and six-hour, 15-minute, and 30-second totalizers.

Isn't it nice when the time machine on your wrist is as powerful and dynamic as the time machine you drive? Together, Bentley's Supersports and new Continental GT and Breitling's Supersports Chronograph and GMT Chrono are in perfect sync.

SAFE

STRATEGICALLY ARMORED & FORTIFIED ENVIRONMENTS

IS THE KEY THAT PUTS YOUR

WORLD AT YOUR FINGERTIP

Learn more about the protection, control and convenience that world class security provides.

www.SAFE-US.com

+202.484.9500

"My dear Veronica" By Philip C. Brooks

This series of letters was found in the glove box of B196HK, a 1936 Bentley with Vanden Plas two-seater body and registration number ALY 605. The letters were apparently from the car to the late Veronica Pearson Tritton, her owner from 1937 to 1955.

My dear Veronica,

It's been decades since we saw each other. When you last saw me in the Brookses' garage, my wings were off, my seats were out, my paint was gone – I was embarrassed! Phil and Sue Brooks, with whom I have lived for many years, spent ages getting me back into the state that you and I would have preferred. I was encouraged when you approved of what they were doing. They finally got me up and running. So, I thought it high time that I reported back to you so that you would know how your old Bentley was doing. We had such fun for so many years that I wanted you to know that I am now once again on the road.

In 2008, I was readied for the RROC Annual Meet in Williamsburg, Virginia, where we all now live. But I was only just ready, having been finished the day before I was to be

Photograph reproduced by kind permission of Veronica's great niece, Lady Emma Barnard

Photo courtesy of Philip C. Brooks and the late Ellis W. Bell

Above: I looked like this when Veronica received me as a 21st birthday present in 1937. **Right, top:** Veronica Pearson Tritton when she owned me.
Right, bottom: Brett loads me onto the FedEx car transporter in Williamsburg.

judged. The Brookses brought me back to the way I was in September 1939, when you had me repaired by those good people at Vanden Plas after our trip to Sweden. They did have me striped in my original red and silver, rather than the broken white that you had done in '39, but otherwise I was just as you specified.

We didn't realize that this new petrol called "ethanol" rots out rubber in petrol systems. But it did, and I felt very ill. Still, I came in second in the "Concours" class for Derby Bentleys, which I thought was nice. We came back to the garage after the meet – the Brookses have put up a very nice garage for me, and it even has a lift on which I have fun riding up and down – and I hoped that I would soon start feeling better. The garage is very pleasant, though of course not as distinguished as my accommodations at Parham Park, where we both used to live.

Phil and several friends sorted out my entire fuel system, and I started to run well. Then they said that I have been invited to a "Concours d'Elegance" at Pebble Beach, California, apparently a great honour. The Pebble Beach officials are featuring a special class of Derby Bentleys, and I am one of only eight cars to be invited. There is also to be a "Tour d'Elegance" around Monterey and down to Big Sur. Apparently if we finish this little run of about 70 miles, I will get extra points at the concours. A drive down the Pacific Coast sounds like good fun! I don't know if Phil and Sue plan to drive me across the country, or put me in a goods van on a train bound for the West, or just what they have in mind.

Yours ever,

ALY 605

Tuesday, August 4, 2009

My dear Veronica,

Today has been extraordinary. Phil and Sue loaded me up with all sorts of tools and cleaning things that they said I might need in California, and then they put a collapsible playpen and stroller for their grandson in my dickey seat. Apparently they are going to California in company with their son, Tony, whom you'll remember as having rocked on the hobby horse in the Great Hall at Parham Park, and his wife, Amanda, and little son, Finn. I wondered how we were all going to get there, for it just wasn't on for four adults and a baby to ride very far in me. I found out what was in store this afternoon, when Phil drove me to a large car park and an enormous lorry that was waiting for me. I was loaded into this lorry, which they call a "car transporter" over here, and snugged down for a long ride. It seems that Brett, the driver, and his son, Frankie, are going to transport me out to Pebble Beach in company with a Ferrari and four Porsches. One of these Porsches is a tractor, of all things. I was a bit concerned when I learned that the Porsches were going out there to be sold, but Phil assured me that we would all be coming back home after the show. So I made myself comfortable along with the Ferrari and we headed west.

The starting line for the "Tour d'Elegance," with the Type 57 Bugatti Atalante coupe in front of me.

We loaded two of the Porsches, including the tractor, at a race track in Virginia. Tomorrow we'll go to Tennessee to pick up the other two Porsches and then go straight to California. I haven't been out of Virginia in more than 40 years, so I am rather excited by the whole idea of California.

Yours ever,

ALY 605

Wednesday, August 5 – Tuesday, August 11, 2009

My dear Veronica,

We've had a very uneventful trip to California. Brett had to unload and reload the lorry every time he picked up cars, but he'd been well instructed how to start me and did a fine job. He's a very good driver, and he and his son took excellent care of me.

Today we arrived in Monterey, California. It's a beautiful town, with lovely weather. We went to the high street and off I came from the lorry again – Brett had to unload the Porsches. The Ferrari and I had a pleasant time comparing notes on roads on the Continent and wondering

The front row of car transporters at the Pebble Beach Polo Field. My transporter is several rows to the rear!

what this "Concours d'Elegance" and "Tour d'Elegance" are going to be all about. We liked the idea of the drive down to Big Sur.

We arrived at Pebble Beach to find ourselves not at a beach, but in the middle of a polo field filled with lorries like ours. There must have been well over a hundred of these gigantic creatures. Apparently this is a special year for Bentleys, Bugattis, Ferraris, and Morgans at Pebble Beach, and we are in distinguished Bentley company. Brett and Frankie assure me that the Brookses will be here tomorrow to unload and prepare for the drive along the Pacific Coast. I can hardly wait!

Yours ever,

ALY 605

Wednesday, August 12, 2009

My dear Veronica,

This morning Brett unloaded me from the lorry onto a very strange car park: the polo field covered in wood chips. It is a far cry from other polo fields I've seen! Phil and Sue arrived shortly after I was unloaded, removed all the personal items and tools that they'd packed in me, and dusted me off. Off we went for a little run. We went past the Lodge at Pebble Beach, many lovely residences, and up a hill onto California Route 1. Route 1 is a famous old road in the West, very twisty, and traverses lovely scenery all along the California coast. We only went a couple of miles to the first petrol station in Monterey, where I was able to get my tank filled. Then a short run around town and back to Pebble Beach and the wood chips. Not much exercise, but I was

able to get up to about 55 mph and stretch my legs a little. Sue was thrilled, for it was the first time she had ridden in me in 32 years.

Sue and Phil dusted me off and cleaned me up. They didn't have to do much, as they had cleaned and polished me before we left Williamsburg. They and their friends seem obsessed with polishing me, and I do not object. They tell me that we are to have a 70-mile run tomorrow, with most of the other cars, through the Carmel Valley and highlands, down Route 1 along the Pacific coast to Big Sur, then back up to Carmel. Apparently we will all be exhibited in Carmel while our keepers settle down to a fancy lunch. It sounds exciting, especially since we haven't been on that long a drive in decades. I'm looking forward to it.

Yours ever,

ALY 605

Thursday, August 13, 2009

My dear Veronica,

Today was the day of the "Tour d'Elegance," the run down the California coast, and I haven't had so much fun in years! I really wish you had been there with us ... but on reflection, I think perhaps you were.

The cars lined up very early this morning. There were 178 cars, so the officials split us into three groups of 60 cars each. I was in the second group, surrounded by a gaggle of Bugattis, Packards, a Cadillac V-16, a few prewar Audis, a Jaguar SS 100, a Delahaye, and a huge Daimler Double Six limousine – one of those sleeve-valve engined cars that used to lay down smoke screens of petrol and oil. Better, there were several Vintage Bentleys, including a few Le Mans team cars, some of the Bentley Boys' cars, and W.O.'s old 8-Litre saloon. There was also a 6-1/2-Litre sedanca de ville that had been the Olympia Show Car in 1929, still in original condition, and still very handsome; it was brought over by some lovely people from Australia. Your father would have really enjoyed the sight of all those Bentleys, since he was always such a Vintage Bentley person. Along with them were a few of the cars in our class: What the Vintage Bentleys provided in muscle we provided in elegance. I felt in very good company indeed. Phil was driving, Sue was in the passenger seat, and their friend Brad Zemcik was in the dickey seat taking photos. Brad bedecked himself in a leather-like racing helmet and huge goggles, and he was really quite a sight!

Off we went with a great roar, along roads lined with cheering people and photographers galore. We went up to Route 1 and over to winding roads through the Carmel Valley, up hill and

We went down the Pacific Coast Highway to Big Sur, a few miles ahead of this location.

down dale. Lovely country, but we all went so slowly: I later found out that the California Highway Patrol was leading the procession at 8 mph! It didn't bother me – I was feeling in top form and running very well – but it really bothered a lot of the older cars, for they were overheating, slipping their clutches, and straining on some of the hills. Eventually we started to cruise more quickly toward the first stop, which helped.

From that stop we wound through more hills, then on to Route 1 and the ruggedly beautiful coast. We turned south for Big Sur and started cruising at all the speed the twisting road would allow. I loved going mile after mile at 50 mph and more. It was so good to be cruising at speed once again.

We went along the coast for over 20 miles, over hills, along the beaches, past photographers and cheering crowds. It was a heady experience. Suddenly, the Bugatti Type 57 Atalante coupe directly in front of us shed its left rear wheel spat! The spat fell off, landed on its inside, and skated across the road to the center strip. The driver and passenger quickly got out and retrieved the wheel spat and were relieved to find it unscratched and hardly dented. That was a startling experience.

Eventually we got to our next stop, the first checkpoint on what turned out to be a rally, and Phil got his badge stamped. The Bugatti pulled in behind us looking none the worse for wear. A Type 35 Bugatti pulled up nearby, snarling madly to keep his revs up and keep running. Then came Vintage Bentleys, the V-16, a Duesenberg or two, and the Daimler. Our keepers all had a nice coffee break, then mounted up for "the off." And off we went, back up the California coast. We moved along Route 1 at a smart pace, and suddenly we saw most of the Vintage Bentleys coming south toward Big Sur. They made a thrilling sight, and I quietly sent greetings to them as they went by.

We arrived in Carmel to another traffic slowdown because of the crowds lining the road and cheering us on. It was exciting to be there. We eventually all parked on Ocean Boulevard, taking up about four blocks, and our keepers went to lunch while we all discussed the morning we'd had. Phil and Sue got their badge stamped at the second checkpoint and found several old

friends at lunch. They sat at the next table to Sir Stirling Moss, but he was so surrounded by well-wishers that they didn't have a chance to speak to him. It was Moss' 80th birthday on Sunday, though you would never guess it to look at him.

After lunch, we drove back to Pebble Beach, through more cheering crowds, and back to the polo field. As we entered the polo field road, we went under a large "Finish" sign draped overhead. What fun! I was ready to do it all again, as I was just getting warmed up. But the organizers felt that human flesh was weak and that people would need to rest after an exhausting 70 miles. So back we cars went into our lorries for a good night's rest.

I do wish you had been along for the drive with us, but as I said earlier, I think perhaps you were. I hope you enjoyed yourself as much as we did today.

As ever,

ALY 605

Friday, August 14, 2009

My dear Veronica,

This morning the Brookses came over to wade in the wood chips on the polo field and clean me up after our adventure of yesterday. I was dusty, and I had been pawed enough to have fingerprints all over me. Phil and Sue dutifully cleaned away, and soon enough they thought I looked quite presentable for the show on Sunday. Phil was concerned that I might have used oil and water and even that I might have dripped oil in a few places. Well, of course I hadn't used a drop of either, but I left him to find that out!

Several Speed Sixes are in a lorry two up from mine, and a nice 3-1/2-Litre Vanden Plas tourer is in a lorry about two down from mine. There is also a splendid Pierce-Arrow with a

Experience the exclusivity of Mexico's finest destination at

FIESTAMERICANA *Grand*
LOS CABOS GOLF & SPA RESORT

Where the desert meets the sea under incredible weather and blue sky 349 days per year, celebrating each night with hundreds of candles and tiki torches; a Mystique-sophistication...

Stay at our Imperial Suite, a beach-front 5,600 sqft residence with pampering hotel luxury services and amenities, to include one of the only 7 WineSPAs in the world, and the exclusive Jack Nicklaus, Cabo del Sol Ocean Golf Course, rated # 1 in Latin America, and within the best 100 in the world.

Perks of Ownership:

As an RROC member, take advantage of a special rate of US 3,000* per night for this incredible residence to include; Private Butler, Exclusive Beach Cabana, two SPA treatments per day in our SOMMA WineSPA, one private sailing tour over sunset to see the famous arch from Land's End, daily up-graded continental breakfast, and hot & cold hors d'oeuvres with International premium brands open bar each afternoon. VIP Luxury transfers in HUMMERS from/to the airport.

Our director of leisure VIP travel, Lorena Canedo, will personally provide you with all details. Please contact Lorena at 011-52 (624) 14-56235, or e-mail her at: lcanedo@posadas.com

FIESTAMERICANA *Grand*
LOS CABOS GOLF & SPA RESORT

World's 50 Best Golf Hotels by Golf Digest (May 2009)

www.fiestamericanagrand.com For more information view our E-Brochure
http://www.fiestamericanagrand.com/loscabosebrochure

* Special Package Rate for a minimum of 3 nights to include US 2,000 dollars rebate per night from regular rate of US 5,000 p/night E.P.

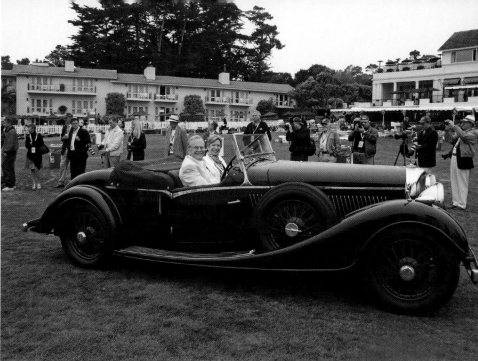

Left: We crossed the "Tour d'Elegance" finish line in high style, right behind a very yellow Packard. **Right:** Very early Sunday morning we drove onto the lawn in front of the Lodge. The parade of cars was rather impressive.

sedanca drophead body by Waterhouse in the lorry next to mine; apparently he's as rare as he is handsome. Across the way are several Bentley Continentals, one a handsome fastback R-type, and a very swish Delage drophead. Ferraris and Porsches seem to be everywhere. And all their keepers are out polishing and scrubbing and doing last-minute things they should have done long before!

I'm all ready for the show, so I'll retire back to the lorry for a good sleep before Sunday's festivities.

Yours ever,

ALY 605

❉ ❉

Saturday, August 15, 2009

My dear Veronica,

There's been nothing much to report today. I slept in, then spent awhile talking to the Ferrari with whom I've shared the lorry the whole way. The Brookses went to a Bentley garden party, but I wasn't invited. I later learned that there were only Bentley team cars at the garden

party, Vintage and Derby models as well as the newer racer that won LeMans a few years ago, and that they were there in conjunction with the launch of a new model Bentley. I thought this was perhaps gilding the lily a bit, but who am I to complain?

I'll write more tomorrow.

As ever,

ALY 605

❉ ❉

Sunday, August 16, 2009

My dear Veronica,

Today was the big day, the 59th Pebble Beach Concours d'Elegance. All of us cars were nearly as excited as our keepers were. We all got going early, as we had to be on the judging field in front of the Lodge at Pebble Beach before 8:30 a.m. Phil and Sue fired me up shortly after

The cool mists of morning did not hide where we were. Sue Brooks looked particularly elegant today.

7 a.m., and we joined a long line of cars heading for the judging field. Again we ran the gauntlet of cheering spectators and photographers as we came around the end of the Lodge and onto the judging field – the 18th hole of the Pebble Beach Golf Course, overlooking the Pacific. A lovely location for a party!

People in golf carts escorted us to our assigned positions, and "class hosts" looked out for us and our keepers all day. Naturally, as soon as the cars were parked, their keepers jumped out and did a last minute polishing dance! I was at one end of the Derby Bentley class: a 3-1/2 Mulliner sedanca drophead, a 3-1/2 Vanden Plas tourer, a 3-1/2 lightweight Bertelli coupe, a 4-1/4 Carlton drophead with a streamlined tail, an elegant 4-1/4 Gurney Nutting sedanca coupe that had been featured in so many advertisements in 1938 and 1939, a 4-1/4 Vanden Plas tourer that was just a few months older than I, and myself. We had been chosen to represent the variety of elegance and significance to be found in Derby Bentleys, and we all felt honoured to be part of such a class. We were an impressive sight, being the first group at the head of the display and next to the ocean – an appropriately elegant location.

Phil and Sue had many old friends stop by to visit, and people enjoyed seeing me; I seemed to be one of the more popular cars at the show. Two friends who came by were the man who has my sister car, B42KT, the one that was built as a copy of myself, and his restorer. You'll recall that car: It's the one you got into once in Bloomsbury thinking it was me!

The day started off overcast and foggy, but later the skies cleared and the day became lovely. The judges came around, seemed to be knowledgeable and fair, and seemed to like what they saw. Frankly, I wasn't concerned one way or another what they decided, as I was just happy to be at this marvelous party. I loved it when two television film crews, one German and one American, came around to film me and talk with my keepers.

At noon there was a commotion up on "the ramp," where the prizes are presented. A very large box next to the ramp was opened, and out came W.O.'s old 8-Litre saloon. Then from another direction came a bagpipe band and two soldiers from the Cheshire regiment, escorting the new Bentley saloon. The new car is very handsome and perhaps a bit understated. It's called "Mulsanne," a name Bentley is reusing. (Names of racing locations are all well enough, but I like names that refer to an engine's capacity, though I must admit to some prejudice on this point.)

That afternoon the awards were presented. Our Derby Bentley class winners were the 3-1/2 Mulliner sedanca convertible, the 3-1/2 Vanden Plas tourer, and the 4-1/4 Vanden Plas tourer that had been parked next to me. I gave her very warm congratulations, especially since her keepers had brought her all the way from Belgium. I don't know how the judges could choose from among the eight of us, for we were all unique and lovely; however, I thought they made good decisions. The "Best in Show" award went to a 1938 Horch convertible with a body by Voll und Ruhrbeck of Berlin, a rather flashy though handsome enough car. It was the sort of thing we were running away from when we went hell for leather across Germany and back home to Parham in the summer of '39!

Eventually this grand show was over. We left the judging field smartly, as I didn't feel like getting caught in traffic once again, and headed back to the polo field. I was surprised that Brett wasn't there with his lorry, but he had been sent off to pick up cars elsewhere. The Brookses loaded me on an equally huge lorry driven by a chap named Don Keithly, who seems both knowledgeable and pleasant. He's an old hand at transporting cars to shows, and he seems to understand me.

And so to bed after one of the great days of my life.

Yours ever,

ALY 605

Monday, August 17 – Monday, August 24, 2009

My dear Veronica,

The trip back home was uneventful, though Don did have to drive that huge lorry all over the country to deliver cars. He's a lovely driver, and I rode very comfortably. I came back in interesting company: two Ferraris (one being my lorry-mate on the drive out), a Nissan racer, a Jaguar XK140 convertible, and that handsome Pierce-Arrow sedanca drophead. We compared notes on our experiences at Monterey, of course. The Nissan had been to the races,

as had the Ferraris; they rather put him in his place. The Ferraris and the Nissan were unloaded en route, and I was sorry to see my lorry-mate leave, as we had become good friends. The Jaguar and the Pierce-Arrow rode with me all the way back to Williamsburg. This trip was certainly the most excitement I've had in many years, but I was glad to get back home. I told my stablemates all about the journey, and I think they were a bit envious!

I tried to acquit myself well and to bring honour to you and to Parham Park, and I hope you're pleased. I did feel your presence while on this adventure, and I hope that we will meet again on another sunny day.

Yours ever,

ALY 605

The trips across the country were different, and the week at Pebble Beach was exciting, but I was happy to be back home with my stablemates.

Barceló Asia Gardens, a place to get lost and wish you were never found.

Barcelo Asia Gardens Hotel & Thai Spa, a unique five star hotel at Spain´s Mediterranean Coast which presents a luxurious fusion of Asian cultures. Bringing the East to the west and presenting the finest blend of Asian therapies, style and cuisine.

At Barceló Asia Gardens Thai Spa, you can enjoy a genuine, traditional Thai massage, a body therapy with over 20 centuries of history, applied here at the hands of experts, graduates of Wat Pho.

The seven outdoor infinity pools of Barceló Asia Gardens, two of which are heated to temperature between 28º and 32º, lakes and waterfalls fuse with the exuberant gardens with 300 botanical species to be found here.

Singita Game Reserves Professional Photographic Safari offers lodging such as the Sweni Lodge, exclusive suites that line the Sweni River in Kruger National Park in South Africa.

STAY and LEARN

By Vera Marie Badertscher

VACATIONS

FAIRMONT Hotels & Resorts keeps tabs on what makes their clients happy, and in early 2010, some interesting research showed that the urge to learn something new does not sleep during vacation. Experience, learning something new, or sharpening old skills took precedence over relaxing.

Consumer research from the Ypartnership, a global marketing communications agency specializing in travel, revealed that almost one out of every three affluent travelers now wants to learn a new skill or activity during a vacation, while a recent focus group of Fairmont Hotels & Resorts' most frequent guests indicates more than 70 percent of those surveyed want to get outdoors and participate in programming that includes a learning element.

That information led Fairmont to start Apprentice-Trips.

"Delivering on this promise, travelers seeking inner fulfillment and a little self-improvement can check in with the brand's new learning-based Apprentice-Trips by Fairmont program. It's a fresh new collection of experiential packages to help guests refine or acquire a particular skill or talent or learn more about an engaging pastime or hobby," the company's Web site says.

Fairmont's experiential vacations span the globe and offer an amazing number of experiences. For instance, learn French in Québec at the venerable Le Château Frontenac (seven-night package); follow the progress of how a bill becomes a law at the Fairmont Washington, D.C. (two nights for

MANDARIN ORIENTAL

Mandarin Oriental, Miami is an urban oasis set on Brickell Key, a 44-acre island in Biscayne Bay considered one of Miami's most prestigious locations. The hotel is just minutes from Miami's international financial district as well as Miami International Airport, South Beach, Bayside and Coconut Grove. The deluxe waterfront hotel boasts the newly refurbished Oasis Beach Club with a private beach, infinity-edge swimming pool overlooking the bay, and sushi & pool bar, and The Spa at Mandarin Oriental, Miami, which is the only spa awarded with Five Stars in Florida. The hotel has a comprehensive fitness center and jogging trail that circles the island, and chic on-property shopping experiences include Karma and Shanghai Tang boutiques, while restaurant options include all-day dining at Café Sambal, the award-winning signature restaurant Azul with a menu of Mediterranean cuisine with Asian influences, and M-Bar, a champagne and martini bar that offers more than 250 different types of specialty martinis. Spacious guest rooms and suites were completely renovated in 2010, and all are outfitted with the latest in technology and include balconies and terraces overlooking the Atlantic Ocean, Biscayne Bay and the Miami skyline. Décor draws on the sophistication of a cosmopolitan city with diverse cultural influences, evoking a serene, residential feel in a tranquil and elegant haven.

Above: Parlez-vous français? Fairmont Le Château Frontenac offers a seven-night Apprentice-Trip that allows you to learn French while taking in the city of Québec. **Right:** Stunning Lord Howe Island's volcanic scenery, jungles, and coral reefs offer the perfect backdrop for Arajilla's outdoor artist retreats.

two adults and two children); or for something more exotic, learn to hunt with a falcon at Bab Al Bahr in the United Arab Emirates (four days). For a complete list of Apprentice-Trips, see www.fairmont.com/promotions/apprenticetrips, or call for reservations: 1-800-257-7544.

Other hotels around the world are expanding their experiential vacations, and here are a few outstanding ones.

AUSTRALIA

Painting Workshop
Arajilla Retreat

Get away to this paradise and make like a modern-day Gauguin, painting away your day in a Kentia palm jungle under the banyan trees. Unlike most South Sea islands, however, Lord Howe Island lies just a short hop from civilization.

A two-hour flight from Sydney, Australia, takes you to this island with dramatic volcanic scenery, the southern-most coral reefs, and a limit of 400 tourists a day. Bring along your charcoal, pastels, or paints and take an art course during one of the four-day artist retreats at Arajilla Retreat. (Students under 18 must be accompanied by an adult, and some prior skill is suggested.)

Only 10 people can enroll in each of the weekend artist retreats that were offered three times in 2010 – June, October, and the end of April. Students can choose to work with one of two artists with very different skills and techniques.

While the 2011 artists have not been announced yet, the caliber will equal past leaders like Australian artist Gary Shead, a prize-winning artist, cartoonist, and film maker. One reviewer sees in Shead, "the formal, thematic and technical strategies in the art of the European masters Rembrandt, Vermeer, Velásquez, Chagall, Dalí and Picasso." His work is displayed in the National Gallery of Australia as well as

Get to know The Royal Shell Islands

Where memories are made and dreams fulfilled

More than 450 privately-owned beach, bay and island vacation condos and houses to rent.

More than 15 years of experience in listing, managing and selling Sanibel, Captiva and Naples properties.

No company knows more about the Sanibel, Captiva and Naples experience and how to make it yours.

Visit us at **RoyalShellIslands.com**

For vacation rentals call **800.656.9111**

For Sanibel/Captiva real estate information call **800.805.0168**

For Naples real estate information call **877.597.7933**

Follow us on Facebook

ROYAL SHELL®

Vacation Rentals | Real Estate Sales | Property Management

Above: InterContinental London Park Lane Hotel's EYE Photographic Workshop offers would-be photographers several "Insider Experience" tours of iconic London sights, wildlife, or architecture.

LONDON

London Thru a Lens
InterContinental London Park Lane Hotel

Snap away on the streets of London and come home with premier vacation photos after you attend this London Thru a Lens photo workshop at the InterContinental London Park Lane Hotel. These one-day workshops work well whether you are a seasoned photographer or just getting started with your new SLR digital camera.

The EYE Photographic Workshop has been set up in collaboration with professional photographer and founder Michael Potter, and will offer guests of the hotel a one-day workshop with a digital SLR camera. Potter's 20 years of experience cover a wide range of photography from home interiors to portraits. His experience providing private workshops and photography services for the wealthy has led to his creation of the EYE workshops, available in locations throughout England and in some European locations.

If you choose to stay at the InterContinental London Park Lane and add the EYE workshop, your portfolio will reflect your choice of nature, history and architecture, or even a trendy fashion shoot, depending on your choice – sights and architecture, pro studio fashion shoots, wildlife in Richmond Park, or plant life at the beautiful Edwardian Petersham Nurseries.

The photo shoot is just one of several options for what the Park Lane calls "Insider Experiences," which enable you to learn more about London while you polish skills. In addition to the EYE Photographic Workshop, Insider Experiences also include a private tour of Borough Market with prolific food writer Sudi Pigott, as well as a true retail shopping experience with design and architecture writer Clare Dowdy.

Guests start in the Club Lounge of InterContinental London Park Lane with introductions and coffee. After a full briefing on camera operation and some basic digital photography techniques, they head out with a professional tutor for a day of shooting. During a working lunch, participants review their work and then go back to work in the afternoon. At the end of the day, individuals return to the hotel where they edit their shots and compile a memorable slideshow on a DVD.

numerous private and public galleries in Australia and around the world.

Robert Malherbe, a painter of people and landscapes, and influenced by masters like Manet and Cézanne, has worked in both Britain and Australia.

Adam Rish's work has won many awards. He works in collaboration with aboriginal painters. According to the resort Web site, "His interest of cross cultural collaboration as 'world art' (like world music) affirms indigenous culture, regional diversity and the possibility of productive intercultural relations."

The artist retreats consist of drawing and painting with the artist in both studio and Lord Howe outdoor locations. In the evening, learning continues with lectures, discussions, and films.

Arajilla Retreat provides a luxurious surrounding on Lord Howe Island, a UNESCO World Heritage Site. The resort is all-inclusive, providing not only your room and all meals, but your paper and canvas, easels, bicycles, and fishing and snorkeling gear.

For more information and inquiries about booking, call 1-800-063-928 or go to www.arajillaartistsretreats.com.

We live

for exceptional moments...

© gettyimages / Martin Harvey

Cox & Kings' South Africa

...we'll help you live yours.

Relax in your Land Cruiser while a cheetah spots antelopes from the vantage point of the vehicle's hood. Witness tens of thousands of wildebeest and zebra rove across the Serengeti Plains. Explore the nearly two millennia-old stone churches of Ethiopia. This is Africa experienced with authenticity, attention to detail and bespoke luxury. With over 250 years' experience, Cox & Kings provides you with exceptional moments that will last a lifetime.

Call your favorite travel advisor or contact us. **1.800.999.1758**

OVER 250 YEARS OF DISCOVERY
COX & KINGS
ESTD ♔ 1758

Exquisite Cultural & Wildlife Adventures℠

coxandkingsusa.com

AFRICA • ASIA & PACIFIC • EUROPE • INDIA & BEYOND • LATIN AMERICA • ARABIA & NORTH AFRICA

Well-known jewelry expert Joanna Hardy offers her insight at the Jewellery Master Classes at the Capital Hotel in London.

When you book your stay at the InterContinental London Park Lane, you can choose the EYE Photographic Workshop Insider Experience as a special package with your room. For information and booking, call 1-888-424-6835 or visit www.ichotelsgroup.com.

Jewellery School of Excellence Programme
Capital Hotel

Joanna Hardy has worked with jewelry for 30 years, turning every woman's passion into a field of expertise that she now shares with others. Besides having worked for auction houses including Sotheby's, Hardy is well known in Britain as the jewelry expert on the BBC's *Antiques Roadshow*.

Fleur Greeno decided to attend a class at the Capital Hotel in London with a friend. Hoping to gain some knowledge of jewelry she had inherited, she came away with many new skills.

The Jewellery Master Class, limited to 14 participants, assembles at 10:00 a.m. Greeno says, "Joanna took us on a journey of how jewelry had changed over the centuries, [from when] it had been sewn into clothing and incorporated in hair, to pieces produced by furniture designers [and] modern-day jewelers."

Hardy points out that she does various lectures on different times in history and the influence of social change and fashion on jewelry. "I have about 10 or 12 different lectures," says Hardy, "most on different time periods. People can come more than once and get new information."

She urges participants to put the jewels in the context of historical events and fashion, asking them to think about the powdered faces, the wigs, the type of dresses worn in a bygone age. The broad-ranging class might cover 1800-1900 in the morning and 1960-2010 in the afternoon.

Greeno explains what happened after her morning class: "After an exquisite lunch came the moment we had all been looking forward to: how to use a loupe! The pieces in the room some of us had brought along were carefully scrutinized and accurately identified."

"Joanna kept everybody riveted: Her knowledge of jewelry is a bottomless pit!" says Greeno, who later organized a class for friends.

The Capital Hotel, in the heart of Knightsbridge, belongs to the prestigious Small Luxury Hotels of the World. It also offers a Master Class in Cocktails and a Fine Art Cultural Experience. The 50 rooms and suites feature traditional furnishings and original artwork in spacious rooms. For further information or reservations, call +44 (0)20 75 89 5171 or go to www.capitalhotel.co.uk.

AFRICA

Professional Photographic Safari
Singita Game Reserves

Photographic safaris appeal to people who want to see the wild game of Africa but have no interest in becoming a Hemingway-style hunter. Indeed, many safaris today go into areas where hunting is not permitted. But what if you are not totally confident about your photography "shooting" skill?

Singita Game Reserves come to the rescue with the Professional Photographic Safari. This collection of nine luxury lodges bring in leading nature photographers to lead four- to six-day safaris, where the participants will sharpen their skills as they go.

While the photographer leading the safaris in 2011 has not yet been announced, travelers will have the benefits of someone who is comparable to last year's leader, Adrian Steirn. The winner of the Nikon Africa Professional Photographer of the Year 2009 and overall winner of the Africa Photographic Awards 2010, Steirn's wildlife photographs reflect imagination and technical skill.

Because the photo safaris take place in most of the Singita lodges, participants have a choice of exploring various ecosystems,

A little bird told me...
"at Tryall, it's eternally 2:15 on the
Saturday afternoon of a long weekend."

...and isn't that just the way you had it planned. Stay at one of the Caribbean's most
distinctive villas and enjoy Jamaica your way. Deluxe & superior villas are available year
round complete with attentive staff and all the amenities and privileges of the exclusive
Tryall Club. Inquire about club memberships, and extraordinary villas and property sites
that are still available. For more information, visit **www.tryallclub.com**, or – reserve your
place in the sun today by calling **800-238-5290**.

Over 80 luxurious villas • Sand, sun & beautiful private beaches • World-class tennis • Championship golf • On-site restaurant
Massage and spa treatments available • Fitness center • Tryall wildlife and nature program • Voluntourism
On-site water sports center • Kid's club and more...

The Tryall Club
*The finest villa experience
in the Caribbean*

Left: Singita Game Reserves Photographic Safaris allow participants to capture nature, such as this African buffalo, through a lens. **Above:** Riad El Fenn provides the luxury setting for a writing class led by British author Raffaella Barker.

MOROCCO

Writing and More in Marrakech
Riad El Fenn

Picture the sensory overload of relaxing on a terrace of a luxurious private home converted into a hotel on the edge of the Medina in Marrakech, Morocco. Ornate tiles decorate burbling fountains, and the muffled sounds and enticing aromas from the bustling shops in the Medina drift into the flower-decked patios. Everywhere you look, your imagination is stimulated: interesting characters, a mysterious setting, exotic customs. If you have ever wanted to polish your writing skills, this might be the perfect place to do it.

The writing class, taught by British author Raffaella Barker, whose novels include *A Perfect Life* and *Poppyland*, focuses on the short story. Students gather for dinner on Thursday evening, and each of the following four mornings is dedicated to writing. After a picnic lunch, the class gathers for discussion.

The hotel is Riad El Fenn, owned by Vanessa Branson (daughter of founder of Virgin Airlines, Richard Branson) and Howell James. In 2005, *Condé Nast Traveler* listed it as one of the Best Hotels in the World. Branson and James bought the main house in 2001 and subsequently have added adjoining houses to make 21 suites and rooms, "connected with secret passages and doors creating a magical mysterious collection of beautiful rooms, courtyards, and terraces."

Your room will be unique. Many have wooden or camel leather floors, some with fireplaces or elaborate tubs. The spa includes a traditional hammam, and guests may relax in a library and a film room.

For guests who want a little more than shopping and relaxing, the luxury hotel also provides a selection of the four-night/four-day creative courses including photography, painting, Moroccan interior design, gardening, and cooking. The package includes your room and all meals.

For additional information and reservations, call 212-524-44-1210 or go to www.riadelfenn.com.

from plains to water to jungle. With only three people per vehicle, each person will have an opportunity to pick what they are most interested in photographing. When not out in the field, the professional photographer will lead workshops on technique, style, and post-production.

Examples of the type of lodging offered by Singita:

The Sabora Tented Camp in Tanzania re-creates 1920s grand campaign-style luxury tents. This camp is very exclusive with six Bedouin-style tents, hosting a very romantic and simple ambiance.

Nestled low on the Sweni River in Kruger National Park in South Africa in the shade of the riverine forest, the six exclusive suites of small Sweni Lodge line the river bank.

Castleton Camp, at Sabi Sands in South Africa, consists of a stone-walled "farmhouse" and six colonial-style rooms that sit in the rolling savannah hills overlooking a well-frequented watering hole. The camp is booked as an exclusive villa and can accommodate up to 12 guests at a time.

One inclusive price includes the photo safari and instruction, all transportation within the country, and all meals. Get more information and make reservations by calling 27 21 683 3424 or visit www.singita.com.

ResortsWest Ski Dream Home

Resorts West has led the luxury accommodations niche in Deer Valley,® and Park City, Utah for over a decade through providing the highest standards in property management and guest services to the destination's most elite clientele. In 2005, Resorts West founders Joseph and James Ballstaedt focused their expertise on real estate development with a project designed to epitomize the ultimate ski home. This vision was realized in 2007 with the completion of the Resorts West Ski Dream Home. Resorts West Real Estate now proudly represents the Ski Dream Home at Deer Valley®. A resort in and of itself, this home is situated in an exclusive gated community and features ski-in/ski-out access to the pristine world-class slopes of Deer Valley Resort.

Just 45 minutes from Salt Lake City International Airport and 20 minutes from the Heber City Private Airport, this exceptional property offers approximately 14,000 sq. ft. of luxuriously appointed interior space and 4,500 sq. ft. of heated decks and patio space with panoramic views. The home features six bedrooms, ten bathrooms and infinite amenities including:

- Outdoor hot tub and heated pool with grotto
- Grand theatre room with 124" screen and leather reclining lounge chairs
- DJ booth and state of the art sound and audiovisual equipment throughout
- Golf simulator
- 550 gallon native trout aquarium
- Two climate controlled wine cellars and multiple wine chillers holding over 1,000 bottles
- Après ski bar and lounge with boot dryers and equipment storage
- Spacious fitness room and separate spa treatment area featuring a steam room and cedar lined sauna
- Fifteen interior and exterior fireplaces and two fire pits
- Multi-vehicle garage featuring car wash and dog spa
- Luxurious finishes including African mahogany, onyx, marble, brunello and hand-made rugs from India and Pakistan and custom furnishings
- Custom designed lighting

Not only does Park City boast The Greatest Snow on Earth™, the destination is also home to North America's #1 Ski Resort, voted first place four years running by the readers of *SKI* Magazine. With unmatched skiing at three resorts, fine dining, art galleries, boutiques and shopping, world-class golf, Blue Ribbon fly fishing, outdoor summer concerts, farmers markets and miles of trails for hiking and biking, this is a true four season luxury resort destination.

RESORTS WEST
REAL ESTATE

resortswest.com

LUXURY ADVENTURE TRIPS

By Vera Marie Badertscher

FORGET the cliché picture of herds of tourists packed on buses. Many traditional tour companies have made their reputations building luxury itineraries and custom (bespoke) trips for individuals or families. Such companies, like Orient-Express, Abercrombie & Kent, Butterfield & Robinson, Cazenove+Loyd, and Tauck, cover the globe. But some smaller companies specialize in one unique locale with the same high level of service. Have a look at a few possibilities. >>>

Dook Photography

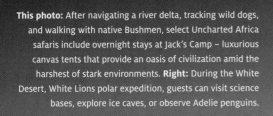

This photo: After navigating a river delta, tracking wild dogs, and walking with native Bushmen, select Uncharted Africa safaris include overnight stays at Jack's Camp – luxurious canvas tents that provide an oasis of civilization amid the harshest of stark environments. **Right:** During the White Desert, White Lions polar expedition, guests can visit science bases, explore ice caves, or observe Adelie penguins.

AFRICA and ANTARCTICA

White Desert, White Lions: Run by White Desert, booked through Bridge & Wickers

Combine an African safari with a luxury stay in Antarctica on what the company bills as "the hardest trip to pack for." Indeed.

In the first four years, White Desert's luxury tours in Antarctica have been limited to fewer than 200 people total. The very first White Desert, White Lions expeditions launched in December 2010.

Patrick Woodhead, with eight polar expeditions to his credit, thought, "It was crazy that the only people who got to see this was explorers and scientists. So we set out to provide a luxury experience for other people. So you could access these incredible parts of Antarctica that nobody had seen before."

A private jet whisks you from Cape Town, South Africa, to Whichaway Camp, your base in Antarctica. On the White Desert, White Lion tour, for eight nights you'll get all the luxury of an old-fashioned safari camp.

Tents, removed after each short tour season, include a main living area with dining room, library, lounge, and communications room. Cozy sleeping tents come with propane stoves.

If that sounds too soft for your wanna-be explorer self, you may choose an igloo for a night instead. Either pitch in to learn the survival skill of igloo building, or watch while your guide builds the igloo. Either way, it will melt with the sun in the daytime and have to be rebuilt the next night. Woodhead says, "If you have a good saw and decent snow, you can build it in about an hour."

Adventure seekers may push boundaries by climbing uncharted ice mountains, go abseiling (rappelling) with a world-champion ice climber, or learn to fly with kite-skiing. There are Adelie and

On the South Africa end of the White Lions, White Desert expedition, guests can catch a glimpse of white lions as they roam freely on the Sanbona Wildlife Reserve.

Emperor penguins to watch nearby, science bases to visit, and ice caves and tunnels to explore – all with gourmet meals and a glass of really chilled champagne each evening.

The guides hold impressive credentials. Among them, Woodhead himself led the first ever east-to-west traverse of Antarctica, covering 1,850 kilometers in a total of 75 days. Ice climbing and mixed-climbing are Stephane Husson's great passions. The guide has about 50 first ascents to his credit and has been a finalist in every ice-climbing championship since 2000.

After 10 days, you may be fantasizing about a place that is warm and green. Just in time, Woodhead accompanies you back to South Africa for a stay at a luxurious Mantis lodge. There, the Sanbona Wildlife Reserve provides a home for the only free-roaming white lions on the planet.

See White Desert's Web site, www.white-desert.com, for shorter or more intensely physical Antarctica trips. For booking this and other luxury adventure trips, check with Bridge & Wickers on the Web (http://bridgeandwickers.co.uk) or call them at +020 7483 6555.

NEW ZEALAND

Maori Culture – Paddle Your Own Waka
Taiamai Tours Heritage Journeys with Ahipara Travel

When you are greeted with the fierce chanting and face-making of the New Zealand native Maori, you understand the power of that ancient culture. Ahipara Travel offers many New Zealand adventures and at the Ahipara-Waitangi Experience, visitors participate in the February 6 Maori celebration of the treaty signed between England and Maori chiefs. It happened in 1840 in Waitangi in the Bay of Islands, north of Auckland.

Rather than a "made for tourism" event, this includes participation in the most important date on the Maori calendar. These northern New Zealand clans, called Ngapuhi nui tonu, have been reaching out to non-Maori since the late 18th century, when they were the first to establish trading links with the earliest European traders. As a *National Geographic* article states, "... as far as Maori are concerned, 'tourism' is just a new word for an old practice – *manaaki-tanga* or mutual respect between host and visitor."

Now a lucky 34 people can join the Mihaka family for a weeklong experience of being Maori. Four days of preparation lead up to the gathering of up to 300 warriors in 20 *waka* (traditional canoes).

The visitor activities are overseen by Chief Hone Mihaka, a huge, fierce-looking warrior with a long hank of hair hanging down his bare back. During the ceremonies, he dresses in traditional loincloth and nothing else but the complex tattoos that cover his body. But the massive body and fierce look are those of a caring person who genuinely enjoys sharing his culture both with Maoris who have forgotten their past and with visitors from other lands.

Above: Aboard a double-hulled *waka*, Chief Hone Mihaka leads guests in the tradition of Maori face making. **Left:** Chief Hone Mihaka expresses joy in sharing Maori culture with visitors from all over the world.

He says, "I give people more than they expect – what we do is not just about a waka voyage or a visit to a historic place. It's about the bigger picture – the things that my people did and believed during those activities or at those places."

Several days of preparation lead up to the Waitangi celebration and ensure that guests will get the most out of their experience. The tour begins at the Auckland Museum for background on the history of the Maori before the five-hour bus trip to the Bay of Islands. While it is possible to arrange 5-star accommodations, the Ahipara company recommends that you sleep as a traditional Maori visitor in the meeting house. After three days of intense training, guests awake at 3:00 a.m. for a dawn ceremony and transport to the waka by 7:00 a.m. Participants will learn to prepare a traditional *hangi* (meal cooked in a pit) and to sing Maori chants.

Ahipara books all kinds of New Zealand upscale tours, including private islands and private jets, catering to those who want the totally unique and private experience. Because their experiences are highly specialized, Ahipara works with specialists in a field, like Hone Mihaka, rather than professional tour guides.

A colorful scene of just some of the underwater flora and fauna that make up the Great Barrier Reef.

To book your own waka, see www.new-zealand-vacations. net/?Ahipara-WaitangiExperience or www.ahipara.com. E-mail: info@ahipara.com. Phone: +64-9-446 6025.

For more information on Hone Mihaka and other Maori adventures he offers, see www.taiamaitours.co.nz.

AFRICA

Safaris by Uncharted Africa

"Driving into the desert at sunset into nothingness because it is a wilderness of open space and light and seeing so many stars my eyes hurt, hearing such silence my ears rang," says Jeanine Louw, a recent guest of an Uncharted Africa safari.

If you are looking for the traditional safari that takes you back to a romantic time when explorers carted their own luxury into exotic territory, Uncharted Africa, founded in 1993, will provide your adventure. One of the many possible combinations might include Game & Water (five nights in Moremi Game Reserve and the Okavango Delta); Sand and Stars (two nights in the Makadikgadi Salt Pans and the Kalahari Desert); and Loincloth and Beetles (three nights with Bushmen in the Western Kalahari).

This itinerary includes visiting the luxurious Jack's Camp, quad-biking in the salt pans, navigating a river delta where you can track wild dogs, and walking with native Bushmen. Animal watching may include sightings of elephants, meerkats, rare brown hyenas, leopards, wild dogs, crocodiles, lions, and cheetahs. The Bushman experience includes learning to cook their meals, make their crafts, and gather wild materials to make hunting weapons and poisons.

Jack's Camp features 10 stylish canvas tents with en-suite bathrooms and indoor and outdoor showers. The tents are set into a palm grove, which creates an oasis of civilization in the midst of the harshest of stark environments. When staying at the camp, you return from each day's adventure to a floor covered with Persian rugs and fine linens on your bed. All this comes with gourmet meals including bread baked fresh each day. Louw describes her meals: "Old World meals, silver service in the sticks – roasted red pepper soup, Botswana beef, and pannacotta with gooseberries. All plated, served meals, no buffet

style, bone-handled, silver-plated cutlery and a true bush experience as opposed to a hotel."

In the river delta, the tour proceeds both by a motorized boat and by native dugout canoe. It was Louw's favorite part of the trip. She says, "... slowly gliding through the water and papyrus looking at elephants on the islands. Also, being in a Mokoro, which is the dugout that gets poled through the winding river by an oarsman who tells you little stories about the frogs and the birds."

The safaris' biologist guides (from the Western Kalahari and Botswana) must have a minimum of at least two years' guiding experience in the Kalahari in order that guests come away with knowledge of the pristine wilderness environment. Louw says, "One day we tracked some African wild dogs for hours and it was so interesting to hear all about their patterns and habitat and behaviour, but mostly because it is told with such enthusiasm and knowledge. The staff are very special."

For further options and reservations, go to www.unchartedafrica.com or phone +27 (0)11 447 1605.

AUSTRALIA

Diving at Orpheus Island Resort on the Great Barrier Reef

Just you and the best stretch of coral on the Great Barrier Reef. 340 of the 350 known species of coral and 11,000 species of fish live around this island, not to mention giant clams. Well, you may have to share with a few other people, but not too many, since Orpheus Island Resort only houses 42 guests each night.

Orpheus Island Resort, a private hideaway off the Queensland Coast of Australia, gives you the perfect location for snorkeling or scuba diving on the Great Barrier Reef.

The resort occupies the only private patch of land on this island, which is dedicated as a national park. All 21 rooms open onto the beach, and when you are not diving, you can keep busy on the tennis court, in the gym, or sailing in a 32-foot catamaran available for guests. Your resort stay includes plenty of opportunities to get in or on the water – unlimited use of motorized dinghies, paddle skis, catamarans, canoes, snorkeling equipment, local snorkel trips, light fishing gear. The national park surrounding the resort means endless trails, bushwalking, and selected interpretive activities will be available if you want to stay on land for a while, and the resort chef will prepare a picnic lunch for your expedition.

If you are a certified diver, you can choose from a full-day diving expedition or a half day. If you are a beginner, take a 30-minute lesson followed by a dive trip.

On the all-day Outer Reef Dive & Snorkel Excursion, ride out to the outer barrier reef, where you spend the day. Take two guided dives, swim and snorkel among all those gorgeous undersea creatures, and then enjoy a gourmet smorgasbord lunch.

Beginners will love Discover Scuba Diving, with a 30-minute shallow-water lesson before the instructor takes you on a controlled dive with limited depth. Those who like it will have an opportunity to continue to work toward certification.

To learn about the nearby rare cluster of 100 to 150 giant clams, sign up for the Giant Clam Experience. Guests tour the James Cook University research station to learn about some of the oldest known specimens of sea life in the world. You can also snorkel or dive among these rarities of the sea.

A mangrove ecosystem presents a unique and eerie environment. The two-hour Mangrove Kayak Expedition allows guests to learn to operate a two-person kayak and then explore the mangroves as you learn about their relationship to the Great Barrier Reef.

No children under 15, no day-trippers, no telephones. Ahh, paradise.

For more information or to make a booking, contact (07) 4777 7377 or e-mail bookings@orpheus.com.au. Further information can be found at www.orpheus.com.au.

MONGOLIA

The Ultimate Gobi Adventure by Nomadic Expeditions

Even jaded travelers come back awed by the grand scenic splendor of Mongolia's three ecosystems – mountains, steppes, and the Gobi Desert.

The founder of Nomadic Expeditions, Jalsa Urubshurow, a Mongolian-American, made a living as a carpenter in New Jersey before he decided to fund a travel company to take people to Mongolia.

Your trip will start with arrival in Beijing, China, which has the most flights into Mongolia. From there you can take one of the planned tours, like the Ultimate Gobi Adventure, Yak and Kayak, which traverses the three ecological zones of Mongolia, or Mongolian Vistas, an overview of the country.

Outer Mongolia, synonymous with "the end of nowhere," became a democratic country, now known as the Republic of Mongolia, in 1992. The country, about the size of Alaska, has only 1,000 miles of paved roads, so on your travels, you will experience some decidedly different modes of transportation. Since Nomadic Expeditions specializes in the remotest locations of this country, you may travel by horseback or ride a camel, in addition to four-wheel-drive vehicles.

Most housing is in *gers*, the traditional domed structures used by Mongolian herders and farmers. Nomadic Expeditions recently built Three Camel Lodge to provide a luxury hotel experience, totally off the power grid, near the largest national park. A large central structure provides a

We live
for exceptional moments...

© Hugh Sitton / Corbis

Cox & Kings' India

...we'll help you live yours.

Be welcomed with a henna *tilak* on your third eye in Rajasthan. Dine by candlelight on grilled game on the ramparts of the Mehrangarh Fort. Or test your polo skills while at Dera Amer in Jaipur while competing against noblemen on the backs of elephants. This is India experienced with authenticity, attention to detail and bespoke luxury. With over 250 years' experience, Cox & Kings provides you exceptional moments that will last a lifetime.

Call your favorite travel advisor or contact us. **1.800.999.1758**

OVER 250 YEARS OF DISCOVERY
COX & KINGS
ESTD 1758

Exquisite Cultural & Wildlife Adventures℠

coxandkingsusa.com

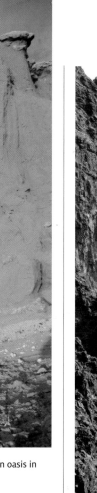

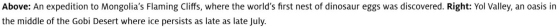

Above: An expedition to Mongolia's Flaming Cliffs, where the world's first nest of dinosaur eggs was discovered. **Right:** Yol Valley, an oasis in the middle of the Gobi Desert where ice persists as late as late July.

restaurant, a lounge, a spa, and showers. The two classes of ger include 20 that provide the luxury of in-suite toilet and wash basin, and 30 others. But the furnishing and bedding equal the comfort of the best African safari camp, according to Urubshurow.

Builders located the Three Camel Lodge on a site well used by herdsmen "so you may sit outside in the evening and see 200 camels being watered at sunset," says Urubshurow. Organized tours, led by Mongolian college graduates fluent in many languages and trained by the company, are limited to 15 people, for maximum personal attention. Those seeking adrenaline-packed adventure should inquire about those times of year when the

rivers are running full and it is possible to kayak down class-3 and -4 rapids four times a day. Camels carry you into the desert to experience the "singing sands." Or ride along with the hunters who train golden eagles to help them hunt, the way Middle Ages Europeans used trained falcons. If you choose a trek that keeps you away from Three Camel Lodge overnight, you will sleep in a tent furnished with comfortable bedding – even a cot if you request it. Because of the totally dark skies, Urubshurow says, "The desert is an astronomer's delight. I call the tent a 5,000-star hotel."

For further information or bookings, go to http://nomadicexpeditions.com or call 1-800-998-6634.

HOW THE OTHER HALF LIVES

Get an inside look at the celebrity lifestyle by renting a home formerly or currently owned by a famous personality

By Heidi Bohi

JUST between us, Mr. Jagger is extremely sensitive about giving out the name of his rental home in Mustique, the exclusive island in the southern Caribbean. So when you call to inquire about vacationing there, tell the property management company only that you are interested in renting a six-bedroom Japanese-style villa beachfront residence made up of six pavilions linked by elevated walkways that meander around the property's lush coconut palms and known, among other things, for its spectacular views of the nearby island over L'Ansecoy Bay.

Don't even breathe the words "beast of burden." Mentioning his name, or specifically requesting the Stargroves Villa, is certain to make Mick uncomfortable enough to deny your application. Yes, the final stamp of approval comes from him. The Rolling Stones rocker, lead singer, and legend of fortune, fame, and womanizing does not let just anyone walk in his world. Or sleep in his bed. If living like Mick is your idea of a fantasy vacation, be prepared to submit a rental application that includes a detailed description of the others in your party, along with their names and occupations.

The elegant – and expansive – Les Jolies Eaux is a private retreat worthy of royalty.

Les Jolies Eaux, the home that Princess Margaret built on Mustique, is situated on a peninsula that looks out to the Caribbean Sea and the Atlantic Ocean.

Part of his sensitivity comes from wanting to maintain the spirit of the island, a way of thinking that everyone here shares. As the locals will tell you, there are no paparazzi hiding behind trees on the 1,400-acre private parcel that offers lush rolling terrain, gentle trade winds, pristine white beaches, and aquamarine waters.

Mustique is known as a haven for front-cover stars and celebrities who, during their downtime, want to leave their limelight lifestyles behind for the rare opportunity to pretend they're just like everyone else. Ironically, for everyone else the island offers the once-in-a-lifetime chance to be one of them. But on both sides of the velvet rope, there is an unspoken code of conduct for the 500 island guests who pay anywhere from $7,000 to $100,000 a week to rent properties that are commonly owned by celebrities who comfortably mix and mingle with everyone on the island, knowing that no one here is gauche enough to people watch.

Jagger's Stargroves Villa, renting for $15,000 to $19,000 a week, is named after his 1970s English country estate and recording venue for The Rolling Stones and other well-known bands and musicians such as The Who, Led Zeppelin, Santana, and Bob Marley. Although he spends a lot of time in Mustique, when he's off touring or enjoying one of his other homes – including a $10.8 million home in Chelsea, London, and his $4 million Pelican Beach property adjoining Stargroves – renters may get the sense that he's ready to walk in the room at anytime, as it is filled with family photos and personal mementos from his career. It is also appointed with a large pool and sundeck, Jacuzzi, koi pond, game pavilion, a Jeep, and six staff who cater to guests. The open architecture allows the Caribbean sea breeze to flow throughout the villa, and inside and outside dining rooms also give guests the option of dining *al fresco* under the stars, with all meals prepared by a full-time chef.

Her Royal Highness Princess Margaret, fashion designer Tommy Hilfiger, singer and songwriter Bryan Adams: Theirs are just a few of the Mustique rental homes that are owned by the rich and famous, or that have a history of celebrity ownership. This is where the other half comes to build their dream homes, which explains why each of the 100 privately owned luxury residences are showcase examples of distinctive styles of architecture and interior design.

The late Princess Margaret was the first prominent celebrity to have a home on Mustique and is responsible for putting the island on the map. Les Jolies Eaux, meaning "beautiful waters," was finished in 1972 and sits on 10 acres that were given to her as an engagement present in 1959 from island owner Colin Tennant,

now Lord Glenconner. In a world where royalty lives according to the rules of the British monarchy, this was her haven of peace where she was free to be herself.

Parties at Les Jolies Eaux were legendary, and lavish picnics and nude sunbathing were commonly part of the day's festivities that included her cousin Lord Lichfield, who had a villa nearby, gangster and rumored lover John Bindon, Mick Jagger, and Roddy Llewellyn, a landscape gardener and lover 17 years her junior. After giving it to her son, Lord Linley, as a wedding gift, he sold it in 1998, much to her distress.

This villa stands on a private peninsula that looks out to the Caribbean Sea and Atlantic Ocean, with spectacular views of Canouan and other Grenadine Islands. Villa facilities include private outdoor porches for each of the five bedrooms, a Jeep, and all bedrooms have their own private deck. Staff may reminisce of days gone by: It includes the cook, who worked for the original owner and who manages the permanent house staff; the butler, who has been at the house for a decade; and the maids and gardener. Les Jolies Eaux rents for $18,000 to $28,000 a week, depending on the season.

Although Mustique has more celebrity rentals than most neighborhoods, it is part of an increasing trend worldwide for celebrities – who are typically protective of their privacy – to open their doors to those who can meet their asking price, whether it is to try and sell their home by offering potential buyers the chance to sample the real estate first, to raise money for a favorite charity, or to offset the cost of maintaining their elaborate homes and keep their staffs occupied.

Many tenants rent celebrity-status homes simply because they like the property and the location, though the glam factor adds a twist that makes the home

LBC

Never Leave Home

Lauren Berger Collection™

The *Lauren Berger Collection*™ *Luxury Boutique Residences*™
makes New York City and the Hamptons your Luxury Destinations.
You set the tone and we masterfully handle all of the details for a
critical Business Meeting, Family Getaway or Romantic Escape.
The Lauren Berger Collection™ combines impeccable service with the
personal touch to meet your specific needs, requirements and desires.
With our two decades of experience, be assured you can relax, enjoy the
hot spots or close the important deal at our Luxury Boutique Residences™.
Additional properties in Greenwich, Connecticut, and
Westchester, New York, also offer the perfect experience at our
Lauren Berger Collection™ Luxury Boutique Residences™.

888 LBC 1099   917 306 5600
LB@LAURENBERGERCOLLECTION.COM
WWW.LAURENBERGERCOLLECTION.COM

Top and above: Both the interior and exterior living spaces of "The Mansion" at Houdini Park are tastefully appointed. **Right:** The 2,800-square-foot former Houdini residence is one of the most famous properties in Los Angeles.

even more desirable, especially with international clients who have not personally seen the house, Patrick Michael, president of Capital Investment Realty Group and LA Estate Rentals, says of his experience representing homes that are currently owned by celebrities, or have been in the past. "The celebrity factor helps play a role in their booking as it brings credibility and a 'wow' factor to a property, giving the house an added intrinsic value," he says. "If it was good enough for them, then it must be really special – that's the mentality," he says.

Laurel Canyon in Los Angeles, and the Bel Air of its day, attracted many celebrities with the creation of the Hollywood film industry in 1910. There they built elaborate English Tudor and Spanish-style homes including the estates of legendary magician Harry Houdini. Michael represents the historic 4-acre Hollywood Hills estate and private park that Houdini once called home, and today it is one of the most famous properties in Los Angeles. Known as Houdini Park, the property includes a dramatic waterfall fed by a natural mineral spring, seven gazebos, and parking for 30 cars. The 2,800-square-foot, three-bedroom, four-bathroom house has three fireplaces and an open plan kitchen, and sits on 5 acres, landscaped with century-old palms and terraced gardens and offset by canyon views.

Known as "The Mansion," it is also one of the most sought-after sites for recording albums, and well-known rock bands including Stone Temple Pilots, Slipknot, and the Red Hot Chili Peppers have rented it for that purpose. The property rents for $1,500 to $2,000 a night, though several renters have refused to return to spend the night after reporting run-ins with a discontented spirit rumored to haunt the property. In 1918, prior to Houdini's occupancy, the original owner's son pushed his lover to his death from the balcony. One of the musicians from Slipknot says he was standing there getting pushed, but when he turned around no one was there. His bedroom door also opened every morning at the same time, and while in the basement "it felt like something walked through me."

DO YOU STILL HAVE EVERYONE'S GARAGE DOOR?

Not everyone understands the difference between a good garage door...and a great one. Since you understand what quality means, as evidenced by the cars you drive, we assume you'll get the point. At Hahn's Woodworking, we don't make everyone's garage door. We make a garage door worthy of the cars it shelters.

A Hahn's door looks as if it were always meant to be there, completing the design of your home. It operates flawlessly every time with its state-of-the-art engineering. It's the kind of quiet and powerful performance you expect from the automobiles you drive, and is crafted of only the finest woods. And a Hahn's door endures like no other, because our artisans seal all six sides of every element of every door.

Hahn's makes garage doors worthy of the cars you drive.

Call 908-722-2742 to discuss your door with our design team, or review our portfolio at www.hahnswoodworking.com

Hahn's Woodworking...Not Everybody's Door

Considering the number of stars who have owned second homes in Palm Springs, it makes sense that more than half of the current owners claim some sort of link to fame. The consistent year-round climate first attracted Hollywood to the desert. Just 100 miles away, it was the perfect getaway for stars when they worked under the legendary "two-hour rule" of Hollywood's first studios, which required actors under contract to be available within two hours at a studio or director's whim. Palm Springs thus quickly became "The Playground of the Stars." The desert was also attractive to film makers because the consistent climate reduced the odds of production delays resulting from rain and fog. By the 1960s, actors, directors, producers, and movie moguls were building second homes there, many equal in grandeur to those in Beverly Hills.

Frank Sinatra is credited with starting a party in the desert that still hasn't ended. His arrival with the Rat Pack, including showbiz legends Dean Martin, Sammy Davis Jr., Joey Bishop, and Peter Lawford, lured beautiful actresses, many who, in turn, built their own desert dwellings. Old Blue Eyes' original Twin Palms estate remains in Palm Springs, complete with a grand piano-shaped swimming pool, stylishly flat rooftop, floor to ceiling windows, and the original bathroom sink, complete with a crack in the basin where he allegedly hurled a champagne bottle at then-wife Ava Gardner. Sinatra often hoisted his Jack Daniels emblem flag on the flagpole once positioned between the twin palm trees, which let his Movie Colony neighborhood cronies know that cocktails were being served.

Today, the 4,700-square-foot estate boasts mid-century-style luxury and historical significance with modern amenities and can be rented for $2,600 a night. The four-bedroom residence is also wired with the latest technology, including wireless Internet and iPod connectivity with surround sound for listening to nostalgic Sinatra tunes that are also available.

New on the celebrity luxury rental market is the Bing Crosby Estate, located in Thunderbird Heights, a private community in Rancho Mirage, California, known as the place for luxury homes of the rich and famous, including both celebrities and former presidents. Often referred to as "the Playground of the Presidents," Richard Nixon, Ronald Reagan, and Gerald Ford all vacationed here, along with Frank Sinatra, Bob Hope, Fred Astaire, Ginger Rogers, Mary Martin, and Queen Elizabeth II.

An avid golfer who enjoyed the Palm Springs lifestyle, Crosby purchased the house in 1952, the first in what would become Thunderbird Heights, with his wife, Dixie Lee. Perched on the hillside in the center of Rancho Mirage, this 7,000-square-foot estate features custom-made furniture and accents from Asian influences starting with the foyer's 10-foot front door to mid-century Hollywood film posters in the state-of-the-art movie theater that seats eight. Pocket glass walls open the great room out to the lanai, creating additional living space with the desert panoramic landscape in the distance. Sandstone flooring is laid throughout the entertainment and living areas to the pool, including the billiards area and indoor wet bar.

The Twin Palms property, formerly owned by Frank Sinatra, features luxurious mid-century style and a grand piano-shaped swimming pool.

Above: The Bing Crosby Estate, located in Thunderbird Heights in Rancho Mirage, California, includes a putting green, a state-of-the-art movie theater, and poolside fire pits in addition to more traditional luxury amenities. **Right, top:** The Villa Grand has the largest pool in Palm Springs. **Right, bottom:** The tiki lounge and bar at The Villa Grand open onto the pool area.

The master suite is 1,400 square feet and has a sitting area with fireplace and an en suite spa bathroom with a second outdoor shower surrounded by glass blocks for privacy. Each bedroom is luxuriously appointed, and each features an en suite bath. Two bedrooms share a second full-size kitchen and a private entrance. The pebble tech pool and spa with adjacent fire pits can be seen from almost every room in the celebrity estate and includes a BBQ kitchen island and patio dining area. A putting green where Crosby himself practiced is also on the property, which sleeps 12 and rents for $3,000 per night.

In a world that is fascinated with celebrities, Rick Hutcheson, co-owner of Vacation Palm Springs, regularly adds to his inventory of 200 luxury rentals in the area: Among them are the Bing Crosby property as well as those that were once owned by Lucille Ball, Tony Curtis, Janet Leigh, and Christina Onassis.

Onassis, daughter of shipping magnate Aristotle Onassis – who was once married to Jacqueline Kennedy – built The Villa Grand, one of the most magnificent properties available in Palm Springs. It features an 80-foot-long pool – Palm Springs' largest – fountains, a sauna, two Jacuzzi spas, lighted tennis courts, and an indoor tiki lounge and bar that opens to the pool and is equipped with a second kitchen area. Seven bedrooms and bathrooms are well separated for privacy, and the formal dining room, with one of two fireplaces, opens onto the terrace area alongside the pool. This luxury home is completely walled and gated with beautiful gardens, lush green lawns, giant palm trees, and a fruit-producing citrus grove.

For those who are more prone to holidays at sea, the infamous 325-foot mega yacht *Christina O* can also be rented for $65,000 to $94,000 per night and is one of the only yachts in its class that can accommodate 36 guests in 19 staterooms. Originally purchased by her father, who then transformed it into a luxury liner, it features a pool with a mosaic floor that morphs into a dance floor, a Renoir, and a grand spiral staircase with a silver and onyx handrail. Entertaining areas include a dining room that seats 40, and up to 250 guests can be entertained on *Christina O*'s canopied decks.

And the history is priceless: Aristotle Onassis' guests on board were some of the most famous and influential people of the time, including Marilyn Monroe, Greta Garbo, Frank Sinatra, Sir Winston Churchill, John Paul Getty, John D. Rockefeller, Eva Peron, Richard Burton, Elizabeth Taylor, Rudolf Nureyev, John Wayne, and his own mistress, Maria Callas. He also hosted presidents and prime ministers and hosted two of the century's most celebrated wedding receptions: Prince Rainier to Princess Grace and his own to Jackie Kennedy.

FinerThings »

Photo courtesy of Tenuta dell'Ornellaia

POINTS OF SAIL
J World teaches sailing to greenhorns and grizzled racers

"Ready to tack?" "Ready on the jib!" "Ready on the main!" "Tacking! ..."

The words ran through my head all evening after a day's sailing instruction on the Chesapeake Bay with my coach from the J World Performance Sailing School. Not only did the rhythm of the words ring in my head, they meant something. After six hours of working the tiller, winches, and other parts of the sailing rig on one of J World's 26-foot sailboats, I'd developed a basic understanding of how to trim the sails and maneuver the boat to harness the wind. I enjoyed the day and came away with a measure of confidence. Had I stayed the full five-day week that J World's Learn to Sail (LTS) course entails, I would have walked away a certified beginning sailor, ready to enjoy the wind and water and well-versed in all the core competencies.

By Eric Tegler

Students enrolled in the J World Performance Sailing School's Learn to Sail program will spend some time in a classroom but should expect to spend the majority of their time on the water.

"We've found, regardless of your experience level, that the best way to learn about sailing is to be out on a boat doing it," John Alofsin explains. Alofsin is the president of J World, America's premier sailing school. Time on the water and a learn-by-doing approach have been the hallmarks of J World's teaching philosophy since the school was founded in 1980. Whether complete greenhorns or grizzled racers, J World students typically arrive at the school, get a brief orientation on what to expect, and head right for the boat.

In a metaphorical way, that makes sense, because without a particular sailboat there'd be no J World. Magazine salesman Rod Johnstone designed his own 24-foot sailboat (the J/24) for racing in 1975. After a very successful race season, he began producing the racer/day sailor under the name J/Boats along with his brother, Bob, in 1977. Since then, Newport, Rhode Island-headquartered J/Boats has sold over 5,400 J/24s, making it the most popular recreational offshore keelboat in the world.

The J/24's near instant popularity and easy-to-sail qualities led the Johnstone brothers' sons – Stewart, Drake, and Jeff – to conceive the idea of forming a sailing school with a racing focus. But as friendly and appealing as the J/24 was and is, that focus shifted quickly.

"It very quickly became evident that there was huge demand for non-racing courses," Alofsin says. "People wanted learn-to-sail courses, but they wanted to do them in boats that were fun to sail and performance-oriented."

Thus J World was established and expanded from its Newport, Rhode Island, beginnings. With its ideal "winter" sailing weather, Key West, Florida, became J World's second location, offering students from the north a great off-season venue in which to learn to sail or refine their racing/cruising skills. As the business became further entrenched, J World schools were established in San Diego, Annapolis, and San Francisco. The logic behind each location is entirely based on the wind and water.

"We're not on the outskirts of Chicago or New York, even though from a marketing standpoint that might be a no-brainer," J World's president explains. "One of the main aspects of J World has always been that you immerse yourself in sailing. You're not just there to take a few lessons. You're there for a course of some sort. While doing that, you can preoccupy yourself solely with sailing because you're in a true sailing mecca. All of our locations would come to the top of

Learn to Sail participants learn by firsthand experience. "The best way to learn about sailing is to be out on a boat doing it," says J World Performance Sailing School President John Alofsin.

"PEOPLE WANTED LEARN-TO-SAIL COURSES, BUT THEY WANTED TO DO THEM IN BOATS THAT WERE FUN TO SAIL AND PERFORMANCE-ORIENTED."

everybody's list if you asked what the top sailing venues in the United States are. They're also fun places to go."

I can personally vouch for Annapolis, having spent most of my life in the area. Rich in its own colonial and Maryland state history, the city on the Chesapeake Bay is a charming waypoint in the Baltimore-Washington, D.C., megalopolis. It's also internationally known for its place in sailing, with a large share of the world's most respected designers, builders, racers, and cruisers calling it homeport.

I arrive at J World Annapolis (technically in the adjacent burgh of Eastport) on an absolutely spectacular mid-September morning. Under the bright blue sky, the school's fleet of J/80 sailboats beckons from the pier as instructors mill about the J World office/classroom building. A group of communications professionals on a corporate outing from Washington, D.C., has gathered under a nearby tent for coffee, pastries, and an orientation from J World Annapolis co-director Jeff Jordan.

Jordan's lighthearted manner is putting the group of greenhorns at ease as I'm ushered away to one of the classrooms, where J World coach Channing Houston has started the morning's briefing with two students beginning their second day of the weeklong Learn to Sail program. As I sit down, the topic at hand is points of sail. Points of sail describes a sailing boat's course in relation to the wind direction. Depending upon its course, a boat can be "head-to-wind," "close hauled," "on a reach," "running downwind," and more.

Houston explains each with patience and illustration. Like all J World coaches, he has a wealth of experience from collegiate racing for the University of Maryland and the University of Chicago to tenure as commodore of the University of Chicago Sailing Club. In all, Channing has 42 years of experience on the water. He can also point to the textbooks from

US SAILING (the national sailing governing body) given to each student, which can be studied in the evening after the day's sail. As Alofsin says, the J World method, particularly with the LTS program, is an immersive one.

There are a couple of concepts with which the students, not least myself, are grappling. Houston imaginatively runs over them again but then points us toward the door. We'll get a better understanding on the water, he says, and he's right.

My classmates each have a modicum of sailing experience, but from the way they ready our J/80 (a 26-foot boat) to leave the dock, it's clear that Channing has already drummed into them most of what we need to get under way. We do it entirely under sail. There is no motor on the J/80, and we make our way around the pier and out into the channel with only the mainsail up and Houston's relaxed direction.

All the J World schools use J/Boats. As J/Boats grew and began to offer additional models, J World incorporated them in its fleet.

"They're tremendous boats to sail, tremendous learning platforms," Alofsin declares. "They really give you the feedback you need to effectively teach sailing. Even though the vast majority of our customers don't sail J/Boats, they still choose to learn with us because of the reputation we've developed over the years."

Reputation is paramount for J World, which does limited advertising. Any business as long-lived and successful operating on reputation must be doing something right.

"Our biggest source of business is referrals from customers," Alofsin confirms. "We're very proud of that. There have been well over 30,000 graduates and we're happy that our biggest source of business is someone saying, 'You ought to go to J World. It's the place to go to learn how to sail or prepare yourself to cruise.'"

J World's roots are in racing and along with basic sailing, the sport still drives the company's business. While J World remains the country's top racing school, an increasing proportion of its students come through the doors looking to go somewhere, according to Alofsin.

YACHTS ARE LIKE FLOATING BOUTIQUE HOTELS .... *an adventure with opulence*

The luxury crewed yachts of the world are probably the best kept secret of the travel industry. They offer an unprecedented potential for a new and different kind of vacation as well as business events and retreats, customized to your every need and wish.

Crewed yachts can be found all over the world – from Thailand to New York – but are mostly concentrated in the Caribbean and Mediterranean. As luxury floating boutique hotels, they offer every imaginable feature like spas, on deck jacuzzi, water sports equipment, a kite boarding instructor or even a helicopter.

They can host 2 – 100 guests and you have the whole yacht to yourself, guaranteeing comfort and privacy. Not only do you get to choose the "hotel" with all your favorite features and staff, but the location and itinerary as well.

You can have breakfast in France and dinner in Italy without ever packing and moving hotel! Are you creating a great family vacation, accommodating many special interests, or designing the perfect romantic getaway? Do you need the right settings for a conference, corporate event or retreat? Are you getting friends together to explore the hidden golf courses of the Caribbean or arranging a corporate tournament? Consider a luxury crewed yacht: The possibilities are endless and there is a right yacht and crew for everything.

At Amazing Charters, we help you to find the perfect solution for your vacation or event. For more than 16 years, we have been gathering invaluable information about the destinations, yachts, and crew and will use our expertise to give you an unmatched personalized service.

Best Regards,
Ulla Gotfredsen
President

Amazing Charters
Tel: 704 257 4766
Email: yachting@amazingcharters.com
Web: amazingcharters.com

"They want to go the Caribbean or Mediterranean, charter a boat, and not have to have a captain. They want the skills necessary to do that."

Those skills include learning to handle larger, more complex auxiliary-powered boats, living aboard, and navigation. Even in this digital age, not all sailboats have GPS gear, Alofsin points out. What's more, it can fail or be unavailable.

"GPS tells you which direction to go to get from here to there, but it's not always good at telling you what lies between the two spots," Alofisin explains. "So students learn to navigate in the traditional fashion with a chart, plotter, and dividers. It's just part of being a well-prepared sailor."

Navigation is not our major concern as we tack our way out the short channel and into the Chesapeake Bay. Making sure we don't run aground and effectively harnessing the light wind is. As we tack out into the bay (essentially zig-zagging into the wind), my fellow students and I are at the tiller, on the mainsail, and jib respectively. We are sailing the boat, working together, relying on each other. Houston not only helps us coordinate the orientation of the sails on port or starboard tack, he ensures we move safely from one side of the boat to the other, avoiding the mainsail boom and other hazards. He stresses that sailing well and sailing safely are the same.

As we continue tacking, I ask Houston what the most common question he gets from first-time students is.

"The first time Learn to Sail students go out in some breeze and start sailing upwind, they usually get concerned about the boat's angle of heel [the angle at which the boat leans into the water]. The person driving might ask me, 'Is this normal? Am I doing something wrong?' If it's really breezy, people might actually ask, 'Is the boat going to capsize?' The coaches always reassure the students that 'J/80s don't capsize.' I sometimes add that not all sailboats are as well-mannered as a J/80."

Channing is right, of course, and I enjoy sitting on the high side of the J/80 as we heel over. As he describes the points of sail again and I work the winches for the jib, I have several "By George, I've got it!" moments. I ask Houston if he recognizes those in his students.

"One of the skills I begin coaching immediately is the manner in which the driver moves from one side of the boat to the other during a tack. I like to refer to that as part of the 'choreography' of sailing. I can run

J/80s from J World Annapolis sail on the Chesapeake Bay. All of J World's locations are in top sailing destinations.

through it at the dock, and sometimes students seem to view it as silly when the boat is tied up. Once we get under way, and especially sailing upwind in a breeze, the driver can really struggle getting across the boat while tacking. I might refer back to the practice at the dock. I will go through the suggested process again and emphasize the benefit of correct timing – not 'rushing things.' After practicing the moves for several more tacks, there often is an 'Ah, hah!' moment; once the student gets a good approximation, suddenly the tack feels much easier than it was before."

After a couple hours maneuvering, we "luff-up" (essentially bringing the boat's bow so close to the wind that the sails begin to flap and we effectively stop) on the water for lunch. It's a good time to rehydrate and relax with my coach and classmates. Class sizes are invariably four students or less at J World, enabling everyone to get individual attention and to work as a small team. The approach is eminently practical as are the expectations J World seeks to foster.

"We are very realistic as far as what we tell people they can cover in a particular format," Alofsin confirms. "A lot of schools will promise you can learn how to sail in two days. That's just not possible, even though we spend up to twice the amount of time on the water that other schools do. We can introduce someone to sailing in two days, give them some skills, let them see if they want to follow through, but to truly learn how to sail, they have to take one of the more thorough formats."

My six hours on the water drives that point home. There's a lot to learn. We continue learning through the afternoon with a series of drills sailing around a set of buoys on points of sail that Houston encourages us to pick out. The repetition pays off, and with every tack and jibe (zig-zag downwind), I feel more confident and have more fun.

While we drill and learn I can't help but reflect on what a beautiful day it is. Elsewhere, we might be stuck in freeway traffic or sitting through another endless PowerPoint presentation. Out here with the wind, the birds, and other sailboats, we're on our own time and we're not merely riding. We're sailing, making our own way with help from nature. It's refreshing.

The end of the day sees us return to the dock, again under sail, this time on the jib (a small triangular sail in front of the mainmast). While other boats come in on their auxiliary motors, T.L., John, and I coast adroitly into our berth under Houston's steady direction. After handshakes and debrief, we part company. John, T.L., and Channing will be back out again tomorrow. I'm thinking about going back myself. And as enticing as the sailing is, so are the location choices. Maybe I'll try my hand in winds of the San Francisco Bay.

"If you know you're going to do the majority of your sailing in an ocean environment, you might choose to go to Newport," Alofsin recommends. "If you know you're going to sail on a large bay, you might go to San Diego. If you're going to sail in a windy location, you might pick San Francisco in the heart of the summer. The variety of our locations is really a positive, but our goal is to prepare people to day-sail, cruise, or race anywhere."

By R. Pierce Reid

O

THE ART OF THE HUNT

On a crisp fall day in 1890, Gerald Faye was up well before the sun. He walked more than a mile from his home to the water's edge and launched his small johnboat into Kingston Bay, near Cape Cod. Paddling into the marshes that line the southern coast of Massachusetts, he carried with him a large canvas bag containing a dozen hand-carved decoys he had purchased that summer from his neighbor, Lothrop Holmes.

COLLECTING DECOYS

Arriving at his favorite spot, he paddled around the flat water, playing out the anchors and cords as he arranged his spread of mallards and mergansers into a realistic flotilla. He carefully left a gap between the decoys, allowing the arriving ducks a place to land right in front of his blind. Paddling off a few yards, he surveyed his spread and, happy with the layout, he paddled back into the rushes. Morning fog was still hanging in the marsh grass as Gerald settled into his blind, loaded his Fox side-by-side with shells, and waited for the ducks to come in to his decoy spread.

As the first rays of sun began to spread over the water, he could hear the ducks and geese begin to stir. The first ducks to pass over his blind were invisible, only their whistles and wing beats were audible as he waited patiently for his hunt to begin.

Minutes later, as if by magic, the sky was filled with ducks. Hundreds of birds, first in singles, then in pairs, then by the dozen, were flying in from every direction. His decoy spread and calling attracted a pair of mallards that turned right into his decoys. As they cupped their wings to land, Gerald raised his gun, carefully drew a bead on his target and squeezed the front trigger.

Opposite: A primitive, hand-carved decoy, probably crafted in the Carolinas. It was certainly some kind of working decoy.
This page: An award-winning black duck carved by Bruce Emerson of Morrisville, Vermont. The feather patterns and painting must be exact, but it's capturing the bird's personality that makes the decoy come alive.

Crack! Crack!

The gavel banged twice on the auctioneer's podium.
"SOLD to the gentleman on the left for $856,000."

At that moment in 2007, the Holmes-carved red-breasted merganser hen, a simple decoy that once floated unceremoniously in the bracken waters of Kingston, Massachusetts, set a world-record selling price for a single decoy.

Today, these humble tools of the hunter are no longer carried in the field or floated in ponds. Carved wood has been replaced with plastic and synthetics.

But the hand-carved decoys used by generations of hunters are coveted more than ever. Over the past few decades, waterfowl decoys have acquired a collector status that rivals masters' paintings and fine sculpture. Decoys are accumulated by those who appreciate Americana, carving, sculpture, painting, and the outdoors. And they have spawned a completely new art as modern-day carvers continue to keep the art alive and take it to new levels.

AN ANCIENT ART

Decoys have been used as long as man has hunted prey. Wherever traces of hunter-gatherers and early civilizations are found, decoys are part of the archaeology.

Waterfowl decoys in North America can trace their history back thousands of years. Before Native Americans had firearms, ducks and geese had to be trapped or shot with arrows. This required hunters to lure the birds in close. By using decoys made of readily available natural materials such as reeds, bark, and clay, often supplemented with crudely carved heads, the native hunters could entice their prey into range. During a hunt, the downed ducks and geese could also be propped up realistically using sticks to enhance the decoy spread as the hunter's success grew.

Some of the earliest surviving Native American decoys were attributed to the Western Paiute Indians and were found in a cave in Lovelock, Nevada, in the 1920s. Using carbon dating, these decoys have been determined to be more than 2,500 years old. And while many of the earliest examples have been preserved in the dry Southwest, decoys were undoubtedly used across pre-Columbian North America.

Above left: A black duck antique working decoy made in Michigan near the turn of the 20th century. Though not highly valuable, it has a beauty all its own. **Above right:** A woodcock on display at the Ward Museum in Salisbury, Maryland. This carving represents the very pinnacle of the modern carver's art.

MARKET HUNTING HEYDAY

For the first 200 years of colonial settlement in North America, duck hunting was a matter of survival. For early settlers, ducks and geese were a staple of the fall diet. Flocks were seemingly limitless, especially along the major Atlantic and Mississippi flyways. Using flintlock shotguns and muskets, settlers regularly harvested waterfowl for their tables. Decoys were made, usually in the dark and fallow winter months, by individual carvers who spent summers working in fields or shipyards or fisheries.

The big change came in the mid-19th century, in part influenced by the explosion in technology brought about by the Industrial Revolution. Rapid advances in firearms resulted in the more reliable percussion cap quickly followed by breech loading guns that used pre-loaded shot shells. The transportation revolution allowed hunters to ship meat from hunting grounds to the exploding urban centers, and the ice-harvesting industry in New England helped preserve meat as it moved vast distances.

Left: This ruffed grouse carving crafted by Bruce Emerson placed second in its class at the Ward World Championship in 2008. Even the apple and the leaves that are displayed with the carving were made by the carver. Below: A punt gun on display at the Shelburne Museum in Vermont. Firing several pounds of shot at a time, market hunters could kill hundreds of birds with these guns. Indiscriminant hunting resulted in decimation of flocks at the end of the 18th century.

THE LODGE AND SPA
THREE FORKS
Ranch

The World's Only Five Billion Star Resort

AT RIXOS HOTELS, YOU MIX WITH THE A-LIST CELEBRITIES...

Rixos Hotels is the holiday address for anybody who desires to feel special, including world-famous stars, presidents, businessmen, and even royalty.

The name Rixos derives from the seven heroic founders of Perge City in 1000 B.C. Rixos Hotels is the shining star of the Turkish tourism industry and is taking firm steps toward celebrity status around the world.

Rixos Hotels offers bespoke and privilege services to its international visitors in its 12 hotels in Turkey and upcoming emerging destinations around the world, namely Antalya (Rixos Lares, Rixos Sungate, Rixos Tekirova, Rixos Premium Belek), Bodrum (Rixos Premium Bodrum), Konya (Rixos Konya), Ankara (Rixos Grand Ankara), Astana (Rixos President Astana), Almaty (Rixos Almaty), Dubrovnik (Rixos Libertas Dubrovnik) and Tripoli (Rixos Al Nasr Tripoli). Rixos Al Nasr Tripoli is Rixos' latest hotel addition and was put into service in March 2010.

Known for its haut hospitality, attentive personal service and fine cuisine, Rixos Hotels received global recognition and top ratings from leading figures and travel associations such as the American Five Star Diamond Award, Condé Nast, World Travel Awards and Great Hotels of the World.

Rixos Hotels is continuing its rapid growth with particular focus on Eastern and Middle Europe, the Mediterranean Coasts, North Africa and the Arabian Gulf region. The group's vision is to maintain its position as the leading brand name in the art of "Haut Hospitality."

A NEW CONCEPT OF SERVICE

The inviting Riviera resorts of Rixos Hotels combine total relaxation with exclusive locations renowned for their inspiring natural beauty and exclusive celebrity crowd; Rixos Hotels owns and operates the most iconic resort and city hotels and villas.

Rixos Hotels guarantees impeccable service 24 hours a day and tailors its services to the needs of each individual guest in a bespoke manner.

REJUVENATE AT RIXOS ROYAL SPA

The signature feature of Rixos Hotels is the unique spa experience in opulent Ottoman style, surroundings and luxury ambience. The spa interior is inspired by Turkish architecture, transforming the treatments into a divine ritual of steam paradise that channels centuries past.

The certified and professional therapist team of Rixos Hotels offer an array of Asian and holistic treatments. Our guests can indulge in hydro-massages and seaweed therapies alongside organic skin and body treatments.

Turkish Baths of Rixos Hotels have been inspired by Arabian Nights, allowing guests to purify their bodies and souls whilst indulging in the ancient Turkish Bath culture. We use the finest selection of fragrant olive soaps and Turkish clogs. In our relaxation area, enjoy fresh juices and herbal teas with a chat or simply a good book in privacy.

UNIQUENESS AT ITS BEST...

TURKEY
Rixos Premium Belek
Rixos Sungate
Rixos Premium Bodrum
Rixos Tekirova
Rixos Lares
Rixos Grand Ankara
Rixos Konya

CROATIA
Rixos Libertas Dubrovnik

KAZAKHSTAN
Rixos President Astana
Rixos Almaty

LIBYA
Rixos Al Nasr Tripoli

RIXOS
www.rixos.com

This confluence of technologies led to the rise of market hunting.

Market hunters harvested ducks and geese by the tens of thousands, getting paid by the pound for meat. Some used gigantic "punt" guns, which were essentially cannons filled with several pounds of lead shot. These hunters would silently paddle their punt guns into gigantic rafts of ducks and geese and fire a single shot that could kill hundreds of birds at a time.

Other market hunters operated on a smaller scale, using single guns and decoy spreads to scratch out livings as professional hunters.

It was during this period that decoy carving reached its heyday, as carvers worked to supply the thousands of people who hunted to live. Factories even evolved in the late 19th century to fill the need for decoys, and today, some factory-carved decoys are coveted collector pieces.

But it was a short-lived era. The flocks of ducks and geese could not survive expanding agriculture, loss of habitat, and industrialized hunting. A dramatic drop in waterfowl populations resulted in conservation measures being enacted to end market hunting, and in the early 20th century, tightly regulated sport hunting allowed populations to gradually rebound. And though carving enjoyed a renaissance as the Great Depression increased subsistence hunting, the era of the decoy was coming to an end. However, even as the demand for working decoy carving was slowing down, the rise of the collecting market began.

THE COLLECTORS

Until the early part of the 20th century, wildfowl decoys were considered tools, not art. They were unceremoniously floated in ponds and salt marshes, repainted each spring, peppered with lead shot and, when too worn out or waterlogged to use, allowed to simply rot away or burned for firewood. Untold millions of decoys succumbed to the ravages of weather, water, and time.

But a few connoisseurs looked at decoys as folk art and as wood carving masterpieces. Among the first collectors was New York architect Joel Barber. Finding a lost decoy near his Long Island boathouse one day, Barber spent the rest of his life collecting and promoting decoys as art. His book, *Wild Fowl Decoys*, is largely credited with starting the collecting movement. Upon his death in the 1950s, Barber's collection of more than 400 decoys went to the Shelburne Museum in Vermont. Today, the Barber collection, on display in the Dorset House on the

A decoy auction, such as this busy one held at Frank & Frank Sporting Collectibles, can be a great place to buy collector-grade examples of the art.

Shelburne Museum grounds, represents one of the finest decoy exhibits in North America.

As collecting took off, decoys began to receive a level of recognition often associated with fine paintings and sculpture. The work of individual carvers became sought out and their individual carvings brought high prices. Regional "schools" were identified and decoys from different carvers and their protégés within these schools were categorized and studied. Today, the works of hundreds of carvers from more than a dozen regions can be identified.

In addition, several museums have grown up dedicated to decoys.

Among the largest is the Ward Museum of Wildfowl Art in Salisbury on Maryland's Eastern Shore. Named after Lemuel and Stephen Ward, two Maryland carvers, the museum showcases some of the finest antique and contemporary carvings from around the world. One of the museum's centerpieces is the Ward brothers' carving shop, which includes their benches, tools, and equipment. The museum extensively documents their unusual carving careers, which spanned the period from market hunting to sport hunting to decorative carving. Today, the Ward Museum is also the sponsor of the annual Ward World Championship,

which is regarded as the premier judged show for modern-day wildfowl carvers. Each year, the carving judged the finest in the world is purchased by the museum for permanent display.

WORKING TO DECORATIVE

While hunting decoys are still popular, most modern "working" decoys are made from plastic, fiberglass, and other modern synthetics. Produced by the thousands for modern wildfowl hunters, these decoys are highly realistic but are never likely to achieve the collector status of antique working decoys.

And yet, carving has achieved a renaissance, and today, master carvers are producing working and decorative decoys that are as coveted as any antiques.

One modern-day carver is Bruce Emerson of Morrisville, Vermont. A police officer and volunteer fireman, Emerson currently carves part-time. In his studio, he crafts both working and decorative decoys as well as miniatures. His carvings have won prizes all over New England and he has won ribbons at the Ward World Championships. A carver for about 10 years, Emerson's work is now residing in collections throughout New England.

Many of Emerson's projects are commissioned by his clients, who have a specific species, pose, or style of decoy they would like. Some decoys are carved life size; others are scaled down, with miniature decoys being among the most difficult to carve and paint. Others come from Emerson's own observation of wildlife and waterfowl and all of his creations find a ready market among collectors.

Most carvings will start with a simple sketch that will be transferred to a block shape. Emerson is very picky about the wood he uses, and will spend hours looking for the right wood for the body and the heads. After creating the rough shape on a bandsaw, the bird is final shaped with chisels, carving tools, and sandpaper. Feet and eyes are added and the bird begins to come to life. In the early stages, both working decoys and decorative decoys undergo similar steps.

After shaping, Emerson's working decoys are sanded smooth, but tremendous attention to detail has to go into the correct shape and into making sure that the decoy floats correctly. Even though most of Emerson's working decoys will never be used for hunting, it is important to him that they are ballasted correctly in order to float realistically. And if the shape is off, the decoy will scare away waterfowl rather than bring them into the hunter.

GUYETTE & SCHMIDT, INC.

Established in 1984, Guyette & Schmidt, Inc. is the world's largest antique decoy auction firm with over $123,000,000 in sales to date. They hold three decoy auctions per year in St. Charles, Illinois; Portsmouth, New Hampshire; and Easton, Maryland, specializing in antique duck, shorebird, and fish decoys, fish carvings, waterfowl paintings and prints, duck calls, and ammunition advertising.

Since 1989, Guyette & Schmidt, Inc. has dominated the decoy auction field leading by large margins in most statistical categories (See "Decoy Magazine"), by which auction houses are measured. Guyette & Schmidt, Inc. has offices in St. Michaels, Maryland and in West Baldwin, Maine.

In January 2007, Guyette & Schmidt, Inc., in conjunction with Christie's, sold the Alvin Friedman Kein Decoy Collection for $2.4 million. In the sale, a merganser hen, circa 1870 by Lothrop Holmes (Kingston, Massachusetts) was sold for a new world auction record of $856,000.

In April 2007, Guyette & Schmidt, Inc. conducted a $5.02 million decoy auction in St. Charles, Illinois, which was the second largest decoy auction ever held.

In January 2000, Guyette & Schmidt, Inc., in a one event partnership with Sotheby's sold the decoy collection of Dr. James McCleery for $11,000,000, which was the highest grossing decoy auction in history. The top lot was a preening Canada goose by Elmer Crowell (East Harwich, Massachusetts), which sold for, the, an auction record of $684,500.

The Guyette & Schmidt, Inc. firm will provide free decoy appraisals to anyone sending a decoy photo and self-addressed stamped envelope.

Guyette & Schmidt, Inc.
P.O. Box 1170
St. Micheals, MD 21663
Phone: 410-745-0485
Fax: 410-745-0487
www.guyetteandschmidt.com

This attention to detail is necessary because, though Emerson's working decoys cost hundreds of dollars each, some of his clients do use them for hunting, preferring handcrafted wood decoys to modern, mass-produced versions.

In creating his decorative carvings, Emerson must get details such as feather patterns, eye shapes, feet, and other details exactly right. Decorative wildfowl carving is all about ensuring not only that the bird's anatomy is exactly captured but that its personality is reflected in the finished carving. So the inquisitiveness of a ruffed grouse or the attitude of a crow must be captured. To achieve this accuracy, Emerson often uses photographs, taxidermy, and even actual birds harvested by area hunters along with his extensive personal observation of birds in the wild.

"Each carving takes on a life of its own," says Emerson. "And no two are ever alike. I don't think of it as art, but more as an ability to capture a bird and make the wood seem to come alive. One of the most difficult parts is getting the feet right. Though you can buy cast feet, I prefer to make my own from wire and resin. Getting the feet exactly right can take hours."

After the decoy is shaped and, in the case of decorative carvings, feathers carved and burned on, the bird must be painted. Painting starts with primers and fillers that will cover up the wood grain. Then feathers and color patterns must be painted on. In the case of working decoys, colors are added in patterns and patches. But for decorative decoys, each feather must be painted and detailed to exactly mimic a real bird. With the painting, the carving comes alive.

"When I started carving, I never thought of myself as an artist," says Emerson. "But certainly there is an element of art in my carvings. But what I think any master carver is really after is the ability to make a carving that displays all the curiosity, instincts, and even attitude of a real animal. It's more than replicating the animal's form: It's about capturing its personality."

TODAY'S MARKET

For the beginning collector, the decoy market can be daunting. Prime examples of decoys from known carvers or from coveted regional schools can fetch tens of thousands of dollars. For the beginning collector, purchases of high-grade carvings should be accompanied by research and caution.

Fortunately, in the late 19th and early 20th centuries, carvings were made in large numbers and not all have achieved high prices. For the beginning collector, inexpensive yet well-made antique decoys are still in the realm of affordability. And as with any collection, purchasing examples that appeal to you is always a good strategy, regardless of price.

One safe way to acquire highly collectible decoys is by purchasing from reputable auction houses such as Guyette & Schmidt or Christie's. There are also a number of dealers, such as Frank & Frank Sporting Collectibles in New Jersey, that both hold auctions and offer appraisal services. Jon Frank, a retired police officer who founded the company more than 30 years ago, is now the lead appraiser and an expert on antique decoys.

"I got into decoys because of love for waterfowl hunting," says Frank, "but I never intended to become a serious decoy collector. I bought my first decoy cheap. It was repaired and had been re-headed, but it appealed to me. And I always pass that lesson on to new collectors today: No matter how good a decoy's investment potential or how valuable it is, never buy anything you don't like. If you don't like it when you buy it, you will never like it."

Having been involved in buying, selling, and auctioning decoys for decades, Frank has an outstanding insight into the marketplace. "Decoys are a lot like antique cars – and the people who collect them are very similar. They appreciate the fact that a common utilitarian object can have a beauty all its own. And decoys were made for a utilitarian purpose. They were made to put food on the table. They were a necessity. Yet this combination of beauty and utility has helped decoys to achieve fine-art status."

Also like fine automobiles, the decoy market remains strong despite the economy. Says Frank: "The market right now for decoys is as strong as it ever was at the highest levels. And new records continue to be set. Decoys can be a blue-chip investment that you can look at every day. But you don't have to spend a fortune to begin collecting. Fine examples still show up in barns, attics, basements, and sheds!"

CAVEAT EMPTOR

As with any collecting pursuit, new enthusiasts should do their research and learn about the market. Many good books have been written and old auction catalogues offer a wealth of information. So popular is the field that there are several magazines and newsletters devoted to collecting, the largest being *Decoy Magazine*, a bimonthly journal published in Delaware.

With decoys achieving such popularity and high prices, however, has come a plague of forgeries. Collectors, new and experienced alike, must use care and common sense, especially at the high end of the market.

"There are forgers who can very closely replicate valuable decoys by carvers such as Lothrop Holmes or Elmer Crowell," says Frank. "So when buying investment-grade decoys, collectors should ensure that they get proper provenance and a good appraisal. Buying from a reputable auction house is another good way to protect yourself." Frank even goes so far as to X-ray many decoys. "You can't hide anything from an X-ray. Repairs, inferior materials, or improper joinery – they all show up and all can be clues to the authenticity."

There is also an entire genre of "modern antique" decoys, which are newly made but are expertly painted and aged to look old. Most carvers of these decoys represent their works for what they are: modern replicas that represent a popular style of contemporary carving. But sometimes these "new antique" decoys can be offered either by the unknowing or the unscrupulous as genuine antiques.

"As a starting collector," concludes Frank, "you can't go wrong with $100 to $300 decoys, even if they aren't investment-grade. And there are a lot of appealing decoys out there in the low end of the market. But if you are going to start collecting seriously, find yourself a mentor and someone to guide you. Sometimes contemporary carvings are the way to start, because you know that they are right. They aren't damaged or restored or repainted or faked. And don't be intimidated to call some of the contemporary carvers! Most importantly, buy quality work that appeals to you."

A REWARDING PURSUIT

From their humble beginnings on fields and in blinds to their status today as coveted collector items, decoys bridge the gap between tools and art, between simple carvings and the work of masters. Owning an antique decoy is to hold a piece of history. In your hands may be the former tool of a market hunter or a carving that witnessed a father and son on a first hunt together. Your decoy may have fed a family during the Depression or have won a prize at a world competition.

Regardless of how the carving was used, they all reflect the hands, eyes, and skills of the masters who carved them. And there can be no greater measure of art than that.

The moment you experience Plato cabinetry, luxury turns to necessity. The beauty of truly *Personalized Custom* handcrafted cabinets enhances your everyday experience and is elegance you can live with.

The Intelligent Choice in Custom Cabinetry

PLATO

SINCE 1893

for the dealer nearest you

For those who live their dreams, Plato offers master craftsmanship, timeless beauty, and luxury defined by desires — a lifetime treasure for your heart. This isn't just cabinetry, it's an art form.

In an effort to capture the serenity and peaceful appeal of a spa, many homeowners are creating customized bathrooms that could rival any spa-like experience

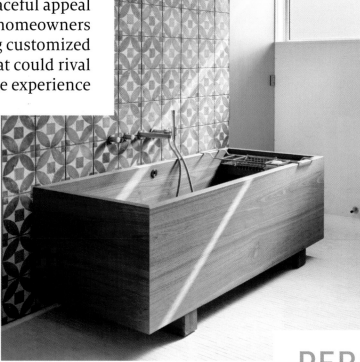

By Tara N. Wilfong

PERSONAL PARADISE

The design of every home's interior speaks volumes about the personalities and affinities of its inhabitants. Artistic groupings in a museum-like space may denote the home of an art enthusiast, while cool, clean lines and functional furnishings express the heart of a modern manse. While the embellishments in these "public" spaces place a perfectly detailed stamp on a home's design, the master bathroom, unlike any other room in a home, provides an intimate window into the homeowners' personal – and private – pleasures.

Taking on a life all its own, the master bathroom often evolves into a luxurious sanctuary filled with amenities designed to pamper and invigorate the homeowner. "Just a few decades ago, master bathrooms were often nothing more than a miniscule box containing three necessities: a commode, sink, and shower," says Norris Broyles, AIA (American Institute of Architects) member and principal of Norris Broyles Architects, Inc., in Atlanta, Georgia. "As the years progressed and homeowners' visions evolved, the concept of a basic necessary room became antiquated and unacceptable. Today, master bathrooms have become more of an environment than a functional space, and they're often viewed as an area of respite, where one can regain their composure, relax, and unwind."

Opposite and this page: More and more attention has been paid to the design of master bathrooms over the years, and many homeowners select fine amenities and add personal touches to create relaxing sanctuaries.

Aside from large, expansive spaces, one of the newest trends in master bathroom design is the concept of his-and-hers bathrooms. Oftentimes, as savvy couples discuss plans for their home's layout, they incorporate the dual necessary rooms so they can both customize their bathroom, creating a space that is inherently personal. Usually situated side-by-side, the rooms can share particular amenities, such as a common shower or steam room, or they can remain completely separate.

"This idea of two separate master bathrooms, each with its own identity and amenities, is really gaining in popularity," says Trevor Abramson, FAIA (Fellow of the American Institute of Architects), design principal of Abramson Teiger Architects in Culver City, California. "The two rooms often share a common vestibule, then branch off one way to her bathroom, and the other way to his. Sometimes the bathrooms are similar in terms of style and design, but we have encountered those couples who want to create completely unique spaces with different fixtures and accoutrements. With the master bathroom, designs and desires can run the whole spectrum, from completely separate to completely united."

A popular solution to the dilemma of separate versus united is one large, unified space that incorporates the best of both

While separate his-and-hers bathrooms have become something of a trend in bathroom design, a large master bathroom with distinct amenities is a popular design concept.

worlds. Blurring the lines of the traditional master bath and adding a functional twist to the trendy separate bath idea, many couples are opting instead for distinct amenities in one large master bathroom. Taking the concept of his-and-hers vanities one step further, these couples customize separate sides of the room to fit their personal needs and wants.

Oftentimes, one side of the bathroom incorporates a soaking tub, while the other is punctuated by an oversized shower featuring steam, traditional, or multi-faucet fixtures. Rarely do homeowners install a tub/shower combination or even a jetted tub, which was wildly popular just a few decades ago. Rain showers, with one large shower head protruding from above, are a popular choice, but Abramson suggests incorporating

"THIS IDEA OF TWO SEPARATE MASTER BATHROOMS, EACH WITH ITS OWN IDENTITY AND AMENITIES, IS REALLY GAINING IN POPULARITY."

additional regular showerheads since the torrent of water produced from a rain head can become intolerable on a daily basis. Two separate water closets and dual vanities, each with its own sink basin, are *de rigeur* in practically every scenario.

To keep the design functional as well as aesthetically pleasing, designers and architects alike agree that the bathroom should contain a central focal point, if not myriad focal points, depending on the view. Generally, the tub serves as that one element that effectively draws the eye and provides the point around which the rest of the design is based. However, a dramatic mirror, customized lighting, and even a picture window with a spectacular view often serve as the central object of focus.

"I love to see artwork or some other object of style and design upon entering a bath," says Darrell Russell, AIA, ASID (American Society of Interior Designers), principal architect for A Boheme Design in Rosemary Beach, Florida. "If there is limited space, a beautiful vanity can serve as that one, central focal point, but in an elegant bathroom, there may be different focal points depending on your vantage point."

For a recent project in Rosemary Beach, Russell created a grand master bath with luxurious flair. The generous space features lofty ceilings with graceful arches, as well as sumptuous materials that beg to be touched. To highlight that one central object that serves as the focal point, Russell included a soaking tub carved from a single piece of Asian statuary stone. This behemoth is striking not only because of its size, but also because of its ability to capture attention as an object of artistic distinction. "When we found this tub in a Washington, D.C., showroom, we knew it was what this bathroom needed," Russell explains. "Once it was placed, it not only served as our focal point, but also the design impetus around which all of the other finishes were based." To add even more drama to this beautiful basin, Russell hung an elegant chandelier with subdued points of light above it, creatively juxtaposing the tub's hard exterior with the cheerful mood lighting.

In the picturesque Western states in which Abramson and his business partner, Douglas Teiger, design dynamic and architecturally inspired homes, perhaps the single most important aspect of

In a recent Rosemary Beach, Florida, project, Darrell Russell incorporated an unusually striking soaking tub (above) to serve as a focal point. High ceilings, graceful arches, and high-quality materials (right) all add to the look of the truly grand master bathroom.

The Thermador Star® Burner adds 50 percent more flame
for better heat distribution and more even cooking.

HERITAGE, INNOVATION AND PASSION
NOW AVAILABLE FOR YOUR KITCHEN

From creating the world's first built-in wall oven, to introducing the first professional range for the home, Thermador has proven time and again it's the brand of innovations for real cooks.

Since 1916, Thermador has enjoyed an iconic presence in the American kitchen with its long list of product innovations. At the same time, the brand has consistently delivered culinary enthusiasts, or those passionate about cooking and entertaining, the ultimate cooking experience with distinctive and stylish products that push the boundaries of convention.

Looking back at a few of Thermador's innovations, which have helped shape the modern kitchen and placed the brand first in the luxury-appliance segment, three innovations stand out.

Thermador made a major splash on the appliance scene in 1947, creating the world's first oven built into the wall. Named the Masterpiece Built-in Oven, the 24-inch appliance was the first of its kind to be recessed into the wall, revolutionizing the concept as we know it today. The design offered consumers the ultimate in luxury, convenience and flexibility.

Forty years—and numerous innovations later—Thermador became the first to reject the traditional round burner to create the Star® Burner that added more flame for better heat distribution. The brand recently improved on that technology with the next-generation Star Burner, which offers 56 percent more output and raised pedestals for easy cleaning. Since its original inception in 1998, the uniquely star-shaped burner has become an icon for the brand's innovative spirit.

And in 2006, Thermador brought the company full circle by revolutionizing the kitchen once again—this time by rolling out the Freedom® Collection Columns, the first modular refrigeration system separating the refrigerator and freezer. The concept challenged convention to redefine what is possible in the kitchen.

Today, the same innovative spirit of pursuing new ideas that keeps things dynamic and exciting has led to the re-imagined dishwasher called the Sapphire,™ designed for discriminating cooks who love to entertain at home.

With cleaning cycles that can handle the most soiled dishes and pots to the most delicate crystals and china, the Sapphire is the best performing dishwasher in the industry with the most comprehensive package of advanced features.

The Sapphire is also designed to be flexible to maximize space for oversized items, and in another first for entertainers, offers the largest wine glass capacity on the market to fit 18 wine glasses. The Sapphire's contoured third rack, called the Chef Tool Drawer,™ accommodates culinary tools and items commonly used by the home chef, while the Sapphire Glow™ Lighting System, with its signature blue illumination, makes the sparkling-clean items shine even brighter.

With Thermador's past and present innovations, the brand has consistently been a leader in the luxury appliance category, creating many imitators but no equals. Targeting those with a passion for cooking and for products designed according to an enduring aesthetic ideal, Thermador offers the absolute best in kitchen appliances that personify its illustrious heritage and is looking to keep that trend intact into the next century.

A user-friendly and water-safe material, glass can add a burst of color in the shape of a sink bowl (left) or art glass tiles or can let in natural light and views or continue the flow of a space when used in doors (above) or room dividers.

in understated, natural hues, the infusion of key items in bold color displays often adds intensity and excitement to the room. "Color is always a very personal decision," Russell says. "I can't say there's a particular trend when it comes to choosing a palette, however, it generally mimics the color scheme that is present throughout the rest of the home. At the beach, the home itself often becomes a backdrop for a collection, so a neutral palette on the bones of the home gives those pieces in the collection the visual strength they should have."

Out West, where a predilection for modern living is a growing trend, Abramson and Teiger encounter homeowners who prefer to make a bold visual statement in their more public powder rooms and embrace the soft tones of nature for their personal sanctuaries. Of course, every calming visage can benefit from an unexpected burst of color. Therefore, in many of their designs, Abramson and Teiger add interest and create drama by infusing color in creative ways. "I don't mind adding small dashes of color to the master bathroom," Abramson says. "It's like a shot of caffeine in the morning to awaken the senses and get the blood flowing."

Unlike any other room in a home, the master bathroom is private and personal. Styles, desires, colors, and themes may vary widely, but inherently, they all remain true to their primary function as components of a necessary room that is designed to please its particular inhabitants. Here, nothing is off limits, including everything from state-of-the-art sound systems to gourmet coffee bars. "In Atlanta, like every other major metropolitan city, I'm sure, there's a diversity of tastes and wants that I believe [is] largely client-driven," Broyles says. "Because of the nature of bathrooms in general, master bathrooms tend to be more highly personalized because they are one of the only private spaces a homeowner has in his or her own home. Guests have the run of the rest of the home, therefore, homeowners are more likely to create a private space that is not only refined, but certainly more specialized and personally appealing."

their designs is capturing the natural beauty of the landscape. This affinity for nature and its connection to the home is often highlighted in the master bathroom, serving as the exterior point of focus. "Because of the intimate nature of a bathroom, we strive to create a tranquil space that is soothing to the homeowners," Abramson says. "Many of them want to focus on their spouse, not a particular element in the room, so we use the view to its fullest potential, harnessing the unique power of nature to create a lovely backdrop and anchor the design."

Adding another dimension to the master bathroom's intimate details, and often mirroring the playful or dramatic mood of nature, lighting plays an important role in the scope of the

design. Soft mood lighting, like the chandelier Russell expertly wove into his design, adds to the allure of the space and heightens the perception of a spa-like experience. More powerful task lighting to illuminate mirrors is equally important, particularly for makeup application. Fixed lighting in the ceiling does little to provide the necessary illumination at the vanity and mirror; however, well-placed lights along the vanity's top edge can be both functional and design-driven.

Once all of the functional and necessary attributes of a master bathroom have been determined, homeowners, oftentimes with the help of an interior designer, set out to personalize the space. While most use color sparingly, preferring to bathe the bathroom

TACTILE TRENDS

Creating a balance between form and function often comes down to the materials palette. In the master bathroom in particular – a space in which relaxation and necessity collide in an abundant display of textures and tones – the chosen materials add significant punch and personality to the design.

Today, perhaps more than ever before, the majority of homeowners are choosing natural products to define their personal sanctuaries. Whether this move is a reaction to the ever-growing green movement or an appreciation for the beauty of these natural products, homeowners are opting for natural stone, wood, and glass to provide stunning visual appeal. "Most homeowners shy away from synthetic materials in their bathrooms," Russell says. "When you're creating a beautiful, luxurious space, the materials should be authentic, highlighting the inherent nuances that make the product spectacular."

Natural stone, such as marble, travertine, and granite, is a common choice for flooring, vanities, walls, and showers because of its durability, general ease of maintenance, and authentic look. Wood, on the other hand, is not generally considered a viable choice for a bathroom due to the wet and chemically corrosive nature of the space, but when it is used in the right application – and for the right homeowner – it can create a dramatic effect.

For Abramson, the use of wood in the master bathroom to create an Asian-inspired, spa-like space is a trademark he regularly employs. A favorite application, in which a slatted wooden mat abuts the tub, adds an unexpected architectural element that is both visually and texturally appealing.

"We've created this wooden bath mat to be soft on the feet and easy to walk on," Abramson explains. "Beneath the mat, which is usually made from teak, is a drain so that the bather can drip-dry. But, because water and wood don't generally mix, we do stress caution when incorporating a wooden mat in the bathroom. If the bather tends to be on the sloppy side, we wouldn't recommend this particular application because of the necessary maintenance that is involved."

For a material that is decidedly more user-friendly and water-safe, many homeowners are incorporating glass not only in the standard applications for doors and windows, but also as a decorative, and oftentimes colorful, element. Traditionally, huge, unencumbered windows are used as a timeless design detail to blur the barrier between the indoors and out, successfully bringing a real sense of nature into the home. In homes situated in scenic locales in particular, a wall of windows in the master bathroom aids in heightening the tranquil and peaceful appeal of the spa-like space.

Equally as powerful, large glass doors and walls designed to cover expansive openings, or section off areas of the room, serve as an elegant, translucent divide that allows the space to flow without cumbersome, opaque barriers. For an added splash of color and fashionable flair, art glass tiles, which are available in a variety of hues from bold and bright to shimmery metallic, provide a perfect accent to walls, floors, and vanities.

Complementing these brilliant bursts of color, many homeowners are opting for decorative glass basins instead of traditional porcelain or stone sinks. Available in a variety of shapes, colors, and depths, the glass sink bowl is an updated and architectural addition to the modern master bath.

With such an emphasis on design, large, furniture-like vanities are making a statement in many master baths. Far from the space-saving minimalism of the pedestal sink – a design trend that has certainly passed its prime – today's version of the modern vanity is a formidable and functional display. Equipped with drawers and shelves galore for plenty of storage and clutter-free presentation, these vanities are often custom-designed to complement the bathroom's décor. "Typically, the vanity, which always contains his-and-hers sinks, resembles built-in cabinetry," Abramson explains. "Since most homeowners want space where they can put their things, we design cabinets in the bathroom that aesthetically mirror the language of the rest of the house, allowing the entire design to resonate with consistency."

Fixtures and faucets are as significant as the space's design itself, and add that special touch to the bathroom. Running the gamut from vintage and funky to sleek and simple, homeowners can honor any design style with a curve of the faucet or the turn of a knob. Finish-wise, there is a propensity for white metals, particularly stainless steel, polished chrome, and brushed or satin nickel, depending on the environment. Golden brass tones are definitely passé and seem to have no place in today's modern designs.

The styles of these faucets and fixtures are also practically limitless, and choosing the right one for any bathroom design is solely based on the preferences of the homeowner. "Each client gravitates toward a particular style or design that they love or desire, and that becomes our primary starting point," Russell says. "It's a lot like that Kohler® television ad when the homeowner says, 'Design around this,' and holds up a faucet. With that one object or design ideal, we can start this journey towards creating something extraordinary."

Since
green actions
have taken on a
patina wrought from savvy
business decisions and tax
incentives, they are now difficult
to sidestep, and putting your
money to work for the greening
forces of good need not mean
corporate losses or Bill and Melinda
Gates' level of philanthropy.

THE LUXURY OF GREEN

I stood alone on the National Seashore at Provincetown, the sea too wide, the dunes severing me from town, feeling so insignificant and overwhelmed within outstretched nature that naked dread sent me scuttling back to Commercial Street to reclaim a comfortable human scale. Awaiting me were coffee and a shop where I chanced on a book of Asian landscape paintings. Tucking a miniscule human figure or tiny monastery somewhere in their depictions of nature's vast majesty, medieval Japanese artists understood the balance of life and portrayed nature as our great mother and home. Intuitively, I saw this as a sign to saunter back over the dunes. Surrounded by winter clouds the color of weathered bones and tin-tinted sea ceaselessly rolling, I felt secure, tucked into my place on Earth, and it was good, the day I turned self indulgently green. "Indulgent?" some may ask. Relax, I'll explain.

By Claudia Jannone

Photo courtesy of Lapa Rios Ecolodge

Along with the conservation of 1,000 acres of tropical rainforest in Costa Rica, Lapa Rios Ecolodge uses local produce, sells only local crafts, and helped to construct a local primary school.

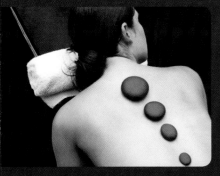

DREAMS CANCUN RESORT AND SPA

BELLAGIO LAS VEGAS

BALBOA BAY CLUB & RESORT

pevonia®
BOTANICA
SKINCARE

Since green actions have taken on a patina wrought from savvy business decisions and tax incentives, they are now difficult to sidestep, and putting your money to work for the greening forces of good need not mean corporate losses or Bill and Melinda Gates' level of philanthropy. Almost everything we buy causes a ripple across the delicate fabric of the world. Luxury goods designers respect craftsmanship and pay good wages for painstaking fabrication, which helps support ethical causes and practices. Stella McCartney designed green before green became fashionable. Giorgio Armani served as Goodwill Ambassador of the UN High Commission for Refugees and his was the first company to join Bono's Red campaign to combat AIDS, with Apple and Motorola quick to follow. Some of Kate Spade's designs benefit Women for Women International in Bosnia. Because indulging in quality helps improve the environment and human lives, our grand and tiny splurges are guilt-free.

Detour with me through a Shanghai market, its stalls festooned with Prada, Gucci, and Louis Vuitton handbags, styles like the Minuit that I had coveted at my local Louis Vuitton store. Rejecting an imitation for vanity reasons, I only later understood my decision's hidden virtue. Behind intellectual property issues lurk third-world sweatshops, child labor, and cruel, slave-like conditions, even suspicion of terrorism. The manufacturing reality behind shoddy construction and hideous design bothers me almost as much as lack of style and elegance. Even some mid-range apparel is produced by cheap child labor, so supporting couture lines helps empower workers and improve the world. Top designers like Jimmy Choo, Christian Louboutin, Manolo Blahnik, and Louis Vuitton work with local and international police in stopping the production of illegal goods that bear their logos, some employing undercover agents who work closely with customs authorities about shipments from countries like China.

Women love shoes, a sweet addiction that reaps green fruit because wise shopping secures good wages for European and American artisans. Parisian cobbler Pierre Hardy, the oft-termed minimalist designer for Hermès, Balenciaga, and his own line, forms a quintessential French example of the inter-relationship between design and craft. Made by people with a long history of cobbling fine shoes, his fetching styles have

One of the designs from Jim Thompson's Benjarong collection of luxury hand-woven Thai silks.

fashionable femmes scaling heights in heels so stark and modern that they look like museum pieces. Every purchase of Donald J Pliner shoes – "handmade in the mountains of Italy" – helps continue the tradition of fine European craftsmanship. Because American shoppers know the "Made in Italy" label signifies superior quality and artistry, high-end U.S. shoe companies have expanded production in Italy. While traveling there, I always visit San Mauro Pascoli, where Romagna cobblers have crafted fine shoes since 1850, and the Riviera del Brenta near Padua, which began its cobbler history around 1200 and today takes workmanship to the cutting edge of design.

Designers of fine menswear look back to a time when men were rugged and no nonsense. For the perfect knockabout lace-ups to pair with jeans or khakis, nothing tops Billy Reid's take on the casual shoe. Reid works with Italian cobblers who hand-distress the leather, achieving a nonchalant yet refined appearance. Beretta, Italian firearm specialist since 1526, enters men's fashion with a line of adventure attire, like its classic safari jacket. Nigel Cabourn, who made his name in the U.K. with hot reinterpretations of vintage, draws inspiration from his father's World War II military gear. His Wilfred shirt closely resembles the tropical khaki drill shirts of Britain's Burma campaign. Taking its wartime cue from America, Gucci reinvents the classic bomber jacket in molten chocolate leather. Cole, Rood & Haan constructs its holdall of sturdy waxed cotton and reinforces it with leather at wear points. The result is an old school weekender ready for the rigor of overhead compartments or a schooner's hold. Burberry's Prosum line has a perfect multi-pocketed top deck or hunting blind parka of waxed cotton. Britain's Simon Spurr is the genius behind Spurr, a sporty denim line, and Simon Spurr, a line showcasing his roots in quality English tailoring and vintage military uniforms.

Nothing sparks home décor like a touch of Oscar, de la Renta that is, whose penchant for modern now includes fabrics for Lee Jofa. Textiles like glimmering silk for walls, textured linens, crewels, wools, and an international range of geometric and floral designs transform a home into a welcoming oasis. Other luxury textiles to redefine the home include Jim Thompson's Benjarong collection of hand-woven Thai silks, and no visit to Central Asia or Turkey is complete without buying a few bright suzanis. Part of a bride's traditional dowry, the hand-embroidered suzani makes a perfect throw. Parisian designer Olivier Gagnère piles suzanis around his Left Bank apartment, tossing two at a time in coordinating shades atop his bed and draping them over a dining table and sofa.

Who would pay $35,000 for a straw hat?

Someone who recognizes a bargain.

Imagine someone weaving, by hand, straw as fine as linen. A single hat can take as long as four months to weave, then two more months for seven other artisans to complete. It weighs less than an ounce, can be rolled and passed through a wedding ring, and looks and feels more like silk than straw.

For more than two centuries, the finest Montecristi Panama hats have crowned the heads of kings, emperors, sheiks, presidents, and prime ministers. Even Napoleon wore a Montecristi.

Today, only nine master weavers remain who still practice the sorcery that turns straw into cloth. I am the exclusive representative, the art gallery, for all nine. I hand block and hand style their works of art into the world's rarest fine Panama hats. My specialty for more than twenty years.

To choose your favorite styles, please visit my website. For personal service, please call.

Master Weaver Montecristi Panama Hats $5,000 to $35,000. Exclusively from Brent Black. Lesser hand-made treasures from $500.

BrentBlack.com (888) 658-6500

Above: Shinn Estate Vineyards erected a wind turbine and installed solar panels as part of its efforts to have the organic winery fully powered by alternative energy. Right: FAIR. offers fine quinoa-based vodka produced from Fair Trade Certified™ ingredients.

All sorts of little luxuries contribute to a greener world. In 1996, the Smithsonian Institution's Migratory Bird Center sparked the shade growing movement. Shade-grown coffee caught on because shaded beans unite superior flavor with environmental gains – bio-diversity, rainforest conservation, sustainable farming, and reduced reliance on chemical fertilizers, herbicides, and pesticides. Unlike hybrid beans, heirloom beans' slower growth cycle intensifies the deep flavor of coffee, returning java and the environment to their roots. Shade-grown coffees and teas work in tandem with the fair trade ideology. Fair trade products – which respect growers, communities, and the Earth – stand as a model for global human connections, justice, and sustainability. Trans-Fair USA certifies grocers such as Whole Foods Market to ensure that farmers receive a fair price for crops, important as many products come from small cooperatives and plantations in the third world. In 1998, the Fairtrade Foundation in the United Kingdom placed fair trade coffee sales there at £13.7 million, which by 2009 had climbed to £157 million. Chocolate and honey demonstrated more dramatic rises over the same period, with cocoa products soaring from £1 million to £44.2 million.

Areas that think global and eat local help to green America because locally grown food reduces the environmental damage wrought by refrigerated warehouses and transporting produce hundreds of miles. I buy mainly fresh and seasonal local produce and splurge on food miles for things not available locally, like Italian balsamic vinegar and New Zealand lamb. Environmentally green actions on Long Island have transformed the North Fork area into an epicurean dream. Often dubbed the next Sonoma, North Fork expanded 20 acres of vineyards to 4,000 acres in just over three decades, and some area wines now snare praise in *Wine Spectator*. Lured by the gourmet trinity of fresh Atlantic seafood, abundant local produce, and great local wines, foodies have begun putting down island roots.

Long acquainted with the quirks of Long Island weather, Mattituck's traditional wisdom held that growing organic grapes there was impossible. Shinn Estate Vineyards disagreed and tried biodynamics – planting vines in rows of flowers and grass to attract the beneficial insects needed to patrol the vines. Fabulous fruit and great wines followed. Winner of a coveted Best Goat Cheese award from the American Cheese Society, the Catapano Dairy in Peconic tantalizes gourmands with fresh chèvre. In response to the growing appreciation for local artisanal products, small creameries keep springing up across America. Whole Foods and other chains now stock a wide selection of artisan cheeses from producers with catchy regional monikers like Cowgirl and Cypress Grove.

On the restaurant scene, mainstream USA has green fever as new bistros create a big city buzz with bills of fare based on local, seasonal, and organic ingredients. The simple idea that "Better is Better" flowered as Chop't, which opened its first salad store on New York's Union Square in 2001, leapt to prominence when discovered by celebrities. With restaurants now

dotting Manhattan and Washington, D.C., Chop't lures hoards of trendsetters and hungry executives with amazing salad combinations. In addition to classic heavy hitters like Caesar and Cobb, its range of organic lettuces, 60 toppings, and 20 dressings let diners create signature meals. It roasts turkeys and beets in house and daily makes small-batch dressings, all fresh, local, and organic – the best. A smiling Salad Dude (Divas too, both trademarked titles) at a Chop't near the Smithsonian composed and chopped my salad while I watched – a huge bowl of health that let me snatch two hours from a packed corporate agenda to see the Smithsonian's Christo and Jean-Claude retrospective.

Even everyday essentials from the big household names – Hewlett-Packard, Dell, Intel, IBM, Starbucks – now flaunt green credibility. The EPA's top 20 green companies and municipalities annually create 736 million kilowatt-hours of green power on site. A *Business Week* story praised Unilever for its floating hospital offering free care in Bangladesh and GE for leadership in wind power and hybrid engineering.

Luxurious green accommodations with no sacrifices now abound. Hotel executives know that customers have a bottom line about green – sure, I want to save the environment while lolling in pampered luxury. Termed "responsible travel" or "travel philanthropy," green travel forms one of the founding notions of ecotourism because it helps alleviate poverty. Properties famous for well cosseted guests span the deluxe destination spectrum – from the digs at top spas to indigenously planned eco-lodges.

Amanresorts won Zagat's 2009 World's Top Hotels, Resorts and Spas honor. I love its elegant combination of high design and first-world benefits for employees, important in developing world wonderlands such as Bali, Thailand, Sri Lanka, and Morocco. Founded on amenities like private pools, indulgent service,

A Rolls-Royce
says you've
arrived.

The bed leaves
no doubt.

E. S. KLUFT & COMPANY LLC
Makers of Kluft and Aireloom luxury mattresses

KLUFT®
THE ROYAL STANDARD

Available at Bloomingdale's
and other fine stores

Inquiries:
909-373-4211, ext. 229 or csandoval@aireloom.com
aireloom.com kluftmattress.com

E.S. KLUFT & COMPANY BUILDS A LUXURY BEDDING KINGDOM ON WORLD-CLASS CRAFTSMANSHIP AND INSPIRED ELEGANCE

While *The Wall Street Journal* and the *Today* show touted the sensational $33,000 price tag in headlines about E.S. Kluft & Company's Palais Royale luxury mattress, the discerning luxury consumer appreciated the story behind the making of the finest and most technologically superior mattress in the world. When Earl Kluft set out to create the top-of-the-line mattress for his "Beyond Luxury" collection, the real story was generations in the making.

In 1959, Earl S. Kluft began learning his craft as a 14-year-old boy in the sewing room of his family's mattress factory in Southern California. Like his father and grandfather before him, the young Kluft became a master craftsman who would design and manufacture some of the world's most comfortable, exquisitely tailored, ultra luxury mattresses, which he and his team of artisans carefully construct by hand.

From this young age, Kluft was driven and inspired to excel in the luxury mattress business, and under his leadership the prestigious brands of Spring Air Four Seasons, Chattam & Wells, and now at E.S. Kluft & Company with the Aireloom and Kluft brands, earned prominence as the highest standard of luxury bedding to which the industry aspires.

For decades, the allure of these wonderfully luxurious mattress brands has enamored those who value world-class quality, including Hollywood silver screen stars and icons such as Frank Sinatra, Rita Hayworth, John Wayne, John Lennon and

Yoko Ono, who are counted among Kluft's many celebrity fans. It is rumored that Nancy Reagan loved the product so much that she furnished each bedroom in the White House with mattresses made by Aireloom.

Kluft continues in his career in the tradition of his forefathers, always taking his craft to a higher level with each mattress he creates. Every mattress to which he gives his name is more special than the last, offering exceptional quality and "legacy craftsmanship" such as eight-way hand-tied coils, hand tufting, hand tailoring and hand side-stitching.

In 2008, Kluft introduced the "Beyond Luxury" collection, featuring the top-of-the line Palais Royale, acclaimed as the finest mattress in the world and the most expensive mattress made in America, sold exclusively at Bloomingdale's.

The Palais Royale is made with the finest materials available in the world, including the highest quality Belgian damask jacquard fabrics, New Zealand Joma wool, Mohair, silk, cashmere, natural Talalay latex, English nested coils, flax and certified organic cotton. At the pinnacle of luxury, the Palais Royale showcases the most outstanding of Kluft's handiwork, technology and design.

With the "Beyond Luxury" line, Earl Kluft raises his craft to a new level of excellence. As he fashions the next generation of luxury mattresses, his signature remains his commitment to quality and his meticulous attention to the exquisite details that comprise a hand-tailored mattress that only he can craft.

and world-class cuisine, Aman reinforces its luxury profile with aggressive community building. So does Evason Hideaway Hua Hin, a respite of posh villas with butlers that also sponsors scholarships for local Thai students. Banyan Tree funds programs for disabled and orphaned Thai children and organizes scholarship assistance for students all over Southeast Asia. Following the 2004 tsunami, some Asian resorts took on a new green glow. Banyan Tree raised $1 million for Thailand's recovery and worked on beach cleanup operations. Long a supporter of Sri Lanka's housing and fishing industries, Jetwing Hotels experienced huge losses, rebuilt, and helped to reconstruct area villages and homes. A year after the tsunami devastated southern Sri Lanka, I listened to shopkeepers praise Amangalla (the Aman resort in Galle) for its quick response. The manager of a competitor resort hotel just blocks from Amangalla confided that Aman had opened its freezers and for days served meals to the community after waves breached the town's levee.

Green actions are growing at most holiday destinations. The spa at the Eco Beach Wilderness Retreat in a rustic stretch of Western Australia uses locally made spa products to detoxify and de-stress. Chaa Creek, a five-star resort and spa in Belize, specializes in local herbal treatments and low carbon footprint activities like horseback riding and jungle hikes. The former Peace Corps volunteers who own Lapa Rios Ecolodge in Costa Rica use local produce, sell only local crafts in the boutique, and helped construct a local primary school. In Istanbul, Hotel Empress Zoe's boutique hotel properties impart high-design elements to guest rooms and flats with antique suzanis on the beds and scattered hand-woven Oriental rugs from area craftsmen. Zoe's Turkish breakfasts pile on the local fresh fare – vegetables, fruits, eggs, cheeses, breads, and jams.

Increasingly, green works to pay it forward in America too, humming sustainability as the new mantra at upscale properties. Papoose Creek Lodge in Montana's Madison River Valley provides the requisite pioneer cabins and outfits them with personal hot tubs, also touting its world-class fly-fishing, canoeing, and wildlife sightings for active holidays with a tiny carbon footprint. Jackson Hole's Hotel Terra combines an indulgent stay with Earth-friendly adventures in a pristine natural mountain setting. The Red Mountain Resort & Spa, St. George, Utah, features leave-no-trace eco hikes, grows its restaurant's produce, and supplies guestrooms

Top: Surrounded by the stunning St. George, Utah, red rocks, Red Mountain Resort & Spa offers guests lovely accommodations, outdoor recreational activities, and healthy cuisine.

Above: TCS & Starquest Expeditions' guests travel in luxuriously outfitted private jets that can adapt to shorter runways at smaller airports, thus avoiding stops that commercial airlines would have to make.

with green products. Maintaining a green perspective has also spread to city properties. In Colorado Springs, the Broadmoor Resort and Spa's golf courses are certified Audubon areas that it maintains with recycled water.

Large volume business hotels now view green as an important marketing strategy, and major players include the usual suspects: Hyatt, Ritz-Carlton, Best Western, InterContinental, Hilton, and Marriott. Some earned Leadership in Energy and Environmental Design certification while others innovated with construction that reduces the impact on logging; vegetated rooftops; community wellness outreach; porous asphalt for parking areas; drains that funnel rain into wells; electric car outlets; and organic bistros.

Air travel brings huge increases in all our carbon footprints, but it is greener on airlines with the newest fleets (Singapore, Emirates, Qatar) because new technologies increase fuel efficiency and lower carbon emissions. Exotic holidays on private jet tours combine educational enrichment with today's tight schedules and benefit the world. The 24-day National Geographic Expeditions visit 12 UNESCO World Heritage Sites, which helps preserve national wonders. Expert lecturers from the humanities bring historical context at stops like Lasha, Tibet, the Taj Mahal, and the Pyramids of Giza. TCS & Starquest Expeditions with lecturers circumnavigate the globe aboard reconfigured, Rolls-Royce-powered Boeing 757s that adapt to the shorter runways at smaller airports, an Earth-friendly way for one hop to replace several on scheduled service.

Thinking green can include a luxury car with a powerful purr. Bentley delivered a manifesto at the 2008 Geneva Auto Salon that presented its stance on the environment, fuel scarcity, and security issues, and outlined plans to enhance luxury autos of the future. While Bentley's contribution to the 3 billion tons of carbon dioxide emitted yearly by passenger cars is small, the company views itself as a model of change. Bentley's commitments by 2012 include the introduction of a drive train with improved fuel economy, improved transmissions, vehicle weight reduction, and engine compatibility with renewable fuels to lower current carbon dioxide emissions.

Naturally, beefing up environmental technologies cannot compromise performance or the luxury details that turn driving a Bentley into Driving a Bentley. Research demonstrated that Bentley drivers like grand touring and need power reserves for challenging motorway conditions. Bentley's bottom line on power goes something like this: Every Bentley must be road rally ready. Unlike brake-slamming Americans, Europeans rely on driving savvy and ready horsepower to pull themselves out of dicey highway situations.

The bespoke automaker must dance on the head of a very small green pin. As Bentley owners often occupy influential positions,

The Arnage, Azure, and Brooklands models' V-8 engines reduced emissions by 6 percent from 2006 to 2007.

they seek a socially responsible stance in purchases, so while the carmaker could offer greener cars through compromises in performance, it refuses to do so at the cost of driver satisfaction and loyalty. For instance, Bentley explored hybrid technology but rejected it because hybrids cannot meet the driving expectations of Bentley owners. While hydrogen and electric drive trains look promising for other demographics, Bentley currently finds they fall short in overall green factors. However, Bentley says that when electricity can be delivered by more economically sustainable sources than petroleum – nuclear, wind, solar, or biofuels – then the company may add an electric model to its design agenda. For now, Bentley pledges itself to wedding social responsibility with its cars' continued prestige and performance levels.

Bentley research already documents a marked reduction in emissions since 2005. The V-8 engine of the Arnage, Azure, and Brooklands models reduced emissions by 6 percent from 2006 to 2007. The company credits three design changes for the improvement: a new 6-speed transmission, revised engine calibration, and a redesigned camshaft. From 2007 to 2008, the W-12 engine of the Continental also improved, dropping emissions per kilometer by 4 percent. Encouraged by these figures, Bentley estimates an increase in efficiency to 15 percent or more by 2012.

The Green Revolution appears to be parked in front of our doors. In some cases it is already lounging inside on a leather Cassina divan with a fair trade designated FAIR. Quinoa Vodka martini in hand as it enjoys yet another summer day with unpolluted skies and a clean conscience. The college kids are on their computers researching Italy's Slow Food movement for a political science essay and reading reviews of Michael Pollan's *Food Rules* for a popular culture course. During dinner, the know-it-all child who celebrates Earth Day may pontificate on food miles and the un-sustainability of eating asparagus that had to show its passport at immigration, remarks that scant years ago might have caused eyes to roll. The private chef, long a master of environmentally focused gourmet cuisine, has dinner on the table with course-selected California wines – seasonal watercress salad topped by gold beets and fresh figs, pasta with basil pesto, grass-fed rack of lamb, baby sweet potatoes with honey and fig balsamic glaze, and shade-grown espresso with fresh raspberry sorbet drizzled in fair trade chocolate. Shall we take our places set with Rosenthal china and Georg Jensen sterling and raise Christofle stems to green as the soft ticks of the cooling Bentley engine ebb to silence in the garage?

The New Arabesque Collection

Boucheron won the 2010 Silmo D'Or, a real recognition in the business, with the model Arabesque BES148.03.

A handcrafted frame with front in laminated Tanganika precious wood and spatula temples in laminated buttered horn and Tanganika.

BOUCHERON
PARIS

www.boucheron.com

GOLD & WOOD
PARIS

Headquartered in the reigning capital of LUX eyewear, Luxembourg, and founded in 1995, Gold & Wood eyewear is known for its exceptional handcrafted designs and has dressed the faces of celebrities like Stevie Wonder, Angelina Jolie, Jamie Fox, Antonio Banderas, Anthony Kiedis, Robin Williams and many

Elegant and rich, Gold & Wood glasses are distinct in their design as each set is intricately tailor made in the Luxembourg factory by 40 craftsmen performing over 100 different operations to finish one pair of these little sculptures.

Made from the most rare and exotic woods and other unique elements such as precious diamonds, buffalo horn, titanium and carbon fiber, each set of Gold & Wood eyewear receives careful attention in its pro

Headquartered in the heart of Napa Valley, BP Wine Merchants is a great resource for enthusiasts, collectors, and investors interested in rare, vintage, and fine wines.

WINE INVESTING

For both collectors and investors, knowing what to buy that will improve is one of the most critical parts of the wine learning curve

L
Like most people who become interested in collecting and investing in wine, it started with an epiphany.

"It was this startling moment when I realized I'd been drinking ordinary wine for most of my life," wine economist Orley Ashenfelter says of his foray into the world of wine that today is a passion, hobby, and, to some extent, a professional sideline.

His moment of truth happened when someone poured him a glass that was substantially different than what he was used to drinking. At the time, he was living on a young teacher's salary. "I didn't have enough money to buy the quality that I wanted, and stealing it wasn't appropriate," he says, laughing, as he recalls his resulting love affair with wine.

By Heidi Bohi

As a Princeton University economics professor, with a few simple calculations he quickly figured out that the only affordable way for him to be able to drink blue chip wine on a pop-top budget was by investing in reasonably priced selections showing the most potential for aging with grace. Making money on his investment was not what he was out to accomplish, he says. But, if he could buy a $25 bottle of wine that in five or 10 years drank like a $200 bottle, his work would be done.

For most wine enthusiasts – and especially for the novice – this is what makes good sense for wine investing, Harvey Steiman, editor at large for *Wine Spectator* magazine, says. The publication is known for its wine reviews and features educational articles on investing and collecting. Every year, it also compiles a Top 100 list that reflects significant trends, spotlights successful regions, and recognizes outstanding producers. Last year, it reviewed more than 17,000 new releases from around the world.

"If what you want is money, there's a very limited universe of what you should be buying," Steiman says. "If what you want is pleasure, then the universe is wide open because you can buy wines that appeal to you, and five, 10, or 15 years down the road, you will be able to share them with friends. That's the pay off."

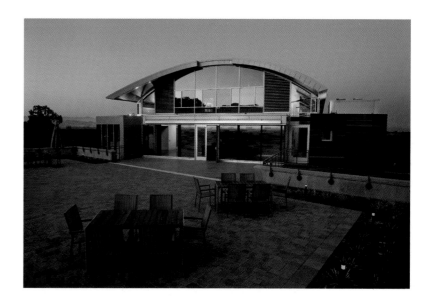

California winery Williams Selyem.

There are two major reasons why people invest in fine wines: as an investment in future drinking, which involves buying young wines at the initial release price which, when mature, are considerably more expensive to buy; or strictly as a financial investment – buying wines with the sole intention of reselling them later for a profit. "Investor" and "collector" are often used interchangeably when it comes to discussing the increasing trend in individuals stocking up on their favorites bottles of wine, often with the hopes of them increasing in value. In fact, there is a distinct difference between a collector and an investor, says Stefan Blicker, owner of Blicker-Pierce-Wagner-Gregory Wine Merchants (BP Wine Merchants) in the heart of Napa Valley. Blicker sells rare, vintage, and fine wines to clients who include enthusiasts, collectors, investors, and restaurateurs from his company's headquarters in Napa Valley.

"WHATEVER I BUY, I LAY DOWN MYSELF, WHICH MEANS AT ANY TIME, I CAN GO DOWNSTAIRS, PULL OUT WHAT I WANT, THEN GO UPSTAIRS AND SHARE IT WITH FRIENDS. IF YOU INVEST IN WINE, YOU CAN'T DO THAT."

Collectors buy wine they love and drink, and they are usually less aggressive about finding the absolute lowest price. While some collectors have been known to dabble in pure investing, that is typically not the case: Most people are collectors and drink their purchases with gusto – or share them with someone they really want to impress. "There is wine investing and there is playing with your bottles," Ashenfelter says, describing the difference between the two enthusiasts and being quick to point out that he falls into the second category.

"Whatever I buy, I lay down myself, which means at any time, I can go downstairs, pull out what I want, then go upstairs and share it with friends. If you invest in wine, you can't do that," he says, because the wine may be off property, or it is cost-prohibitive to drink because of the increase in value.

For the "ordinary wine collectors," which is the bigger group, Ashenfelter says there are three primary ways to buy wine. California wines account for 90 percent of American wine production and consumption. For these wines, he recommends getting on mailing lists of all the famous wineries in the state, such as Williams Selyem, Harlan Estate, and Colgin Cellars, since for many this is their only retail outlet.

High-end wine shops and grocery stores he likes to buy from include K&L Wine Merchants in San Francisco, and in New York: Morrell & Company Wine Store, Sherry-Lehmann, and Zachys Wine & Liquor. Ashenfelter also recommends the Internet, which has become an increasingly popular source as wineries sell directly to consumers as a cost-savings measure.

Continued on page 155

Foppiano
A TRUE REFLECTION
OF THE RUSSIAN RIVER VALLEY

THE TASTE OF FAMILY TRADITION

....

Nestled in the rolling hills of Sonoma County sits Foppiano Vineyards, a 160-acre family estate in the acclaimed Russian River Valley. Cool morning fog and warm summer days create the ideal microclimate for grapes where we have been growing the highest quality fruit since 1896. Today, our winemakers specialize in five elegant varietals, including Sauvignon Blanc, Chardonnay, Pinot Noir and our signature bottling: the bold and opulent Petite Sirah.

Using the fruit of Foppiano's sprawling old vine vineyards, we have earned wide recognition year after year as one of the country's top producers of Petite Sirah. Our fine collection of older vintages allows winery guests to enjoy exclusive tastings of what Louis J. Foppiano calls a "noble" wine. Be our special guest at the winery and taste our family's heritage.

....

Foppiano
VINEYARDS

www.foppiano.com • 707.433.7272

© 2010 Foppiano Vineyards, Healdsburg, CA

INTRODUCING THE FOPPIANO
2008 RUSSIAN RIVER VALLEY
ESTATE PETITE SIRAH

Continued from page 151

Online commercial auctions are another buying outlet that is becoming widespread in the United States. For this buying venue, his top picks are Bonhams Wine Department, specializing in fine, rare collectible, and affordable wines, champagne, port, Madeira, and cognac; Christie's International Wine Department, which sold $51 million in product last year, putting it at the front of the international wine auction market; and Sotheby's Wine Department, known for its sales in London, New York, and Hong Kong, featuring fine and rare wines for both current drinking and cellaring.

When Steiman is not writing about the finer things in life – he specializes in the science of food and wine pairing – he also enjoys collecting wines for his personal cellar that holds about 800 bottles. Because he is able to taste a lot of wines for his work, instead of using investing dollars to buy wines he wants to drink every day, he invests for special occasions with an eye toward his selections getting better over time. Since he reviews wines from Washington, Oregon, Australia, and New Zealand, vineyards from these areas are what currently have his attention. Although many of the wines coming out of these emerging regions do not have a track record yet, he is usually able to make choices that turn out well because he has the advantage of being able to taste so many wines. For the average enthusiast, though, he recommends finding a critic who likes the same styles of wine, paying close attention to their recommendations – and warnings – and using the critic's experience as a litmus test.

At the same time, there are also mistakes to avoid when selecting wines, whether they are being bought for eventual drinking enjoyment or as an investment that will hopefully turn a profit. This includes giving too much credence to what prominent critics say, without considering what the performance of the wine has been since its release. A good example of this, Steiman says, can be seen with California wines in the 1990s, which many investors grabbed up by the cases, only to find that they did not have staying power.

"A wine may be good now, but if you want to put it in your cellar, it needs to have a track record," Steiman reminds. "When you're guessing or using your instincts to determine if a wine will get better, you'll be wrong a good part of the time." At the same time, if the collector stays ahead of the curve and is willing to take chances knowing that some selections will turn out to be duds, it could result in buying a product that improves and increases in value as it ages. "That's part of the game," he says.

Known as a producer of Super Tuscan wine, Tenuta dell'Ornellaia is an Italian winery in the DOC Bolgheri in Toscana.

"The biggest mistake is to buy the flavor of the month. Certain wines get to be darlings and buyers expect more from a wine than it can really deliver," Steiman says.

Only about 3 to 5 percent of all wines produced in the world are collectible, with the rest being intended for immediate consumption, and 11 percent of the population drinks 88 percent of the wine produced. Although wines that appreciate also improve, those that improve do not necessarily appreciate because appreciation is based on what the buyer is willing to pay in the future, as a function of availability and demand.

For both collectors and investors, knowing what to buy that will improve is one of the most critical parts of the wine learning curve. Industry experts unanimously agree that red wines from the Bordeaux region of France – primarily blends of Cabernet Sauvignon, Merlot, and Cabernet Franc – are always a safe bet because they are known for mellowing with age, and the vintages range from everyday table wine to some of the most expensive and prestigious wines in the world, 90 percent of which come from this area, Steiman says. Sauternes, port, white and red Burgundy, and California red wines are also on his list, along with several Italian selections such as Barolo and Barbaresco, Brunello di Montalcino, and "Super Tuscans," which describes any Tuscan red wine that does not adhere to traditional blending standards for the region, such as Chianti Classico wines made from a mixture of grapes with Sangiovese as the dominant varietal in the blend. Recommendations from Spain include Vega Sicilia and several from the Priorat county area, southwest of Catalonia where Cariñena and Garnacha are the dominant grapes.

For serious investors who buy wine hoping that the gamble pays off handsomely when they sell, they see their selections strictly as a financial investment and buy wines with the sole intention of reselling them later for a profit. They are in it almost exclusively for the money – and often do not care if the wine is good, or if they even like it – as their wine purchases are not to be consumed, but to eventually be sold. Purchasing decisions often reflect variables such as limited production and scores it has received from the media, and similar to buying stock, the investor wants to buy low and sell high, treating the wine like a commodity.

To those thinking of investing in wine with hopes of turning a profit, Steiman recommends: "The first thing you have to ask yourself is how important it is that you be able to earn a dollar profit out of investing in wine. And that's tricky to do."

There are no guarantees in the world of wine, whether collecting for improved drinking or investing for a cash return. Wine is an up-and-down product produced from grapes of many varieties grown in different regions under diverse and inconsistent agronomic and climatic conditions, which vary from location to location and year to year. The wide range of wine products and prices reflect these unpredictable variables.

A typical monthly order for a serious collector, Blicker says, is about $2,000 to $5,000. For the serious investor, this tab jumps dramatically to a range of $10,000 to $50,000 every month, and typical purchases may include first growth Bordeaux, Lafite, Latour, Mouton, Petrus, and smaller production wines with Bordeaux properties, such as Pavie, Le Pin, and Lafleur. California cult wines – those for which committed enthusiasts will pay top dollar – include Harlan Estate, Sine Qua Non, Screaming Eagle, Scarecrow, and Colgin. High scoring Italian wines are Giacosa, Conterno, and Gaja, and for Burgundies Domaine de la Romanee-Conti (DRC), known as the "holy grail," though Coche-Dury, Jayer, and Leroy are also in hot demand.

Blicker has one customer who he has never met in person, or even talked to over the phone, but who regularly e-mails orders between $5,000 and $10,000, paying about $500 per bottle. In this case, Blicker says, he suspects that while the client is making great investments, based on the selections he also probably drinks some of his purchases.

When considering different wines, it is not uncommon for consumers to rely on many sources of information, though they may ultimately make the purchase without the benefit of even tasting it. To a great extent, the price of any wine – as is the case with most consumables – reflects quality as perceived by consumers, though in most cases, this comparison of wines is made without the benefit of any real expertise or knowing the quality relative to other wines. Although prices should be correlated to quality – or, it stands to reason, consumers would be spending less for a better quality alternative – and not to perceptions of quality created by marketers, consumers ultimately evaluate quality based on what they're willing to spend.

There are collectors of wine labels who don't consume wine and consumers of wine who base their purchases entirely on the appeal of the labels. For most investors and collectors, the label is often the only resource a buyer will use as a standard source of information to evaluate the wine before deciding to buy it. Although certain information is typically included, such as the country of origin, quality, type of wine, alcohol content, producer, bottler, or importer, beyond that, there is little label

information that tells how the product may be expected to taste. In addition, understanding wine labels can be difficult and intimidating for those who are primarily interested in information such as a description of perceived flavors, taste identification, aromas, acidity, structure, and balance. The consumer is better served by initially knowing the basic facts required on wine labels, then understanding what aromas and flavors to expect from a region, and finally considering how this information comes together in the taste beneath the cork.

Although front-of-the bottle labels undergo more regulatory and creative scrutiny than any label on any other commodity, back labels are completely unregulated, offering producers one of the few opportunities to be creative in their descriptions. Most, though, have nothing more than buzz words, rather than presenting actual notes based on an unbiased tasting of the contents. Some vineyards go without a back label and, in fact, they are extremely rare in Bordeaux, Burgundy, and other classic French regions.

Vega Sicilia Único 1989. Vega Sicilia is a great choice for both collectors and investors.

There is no clear definition of what price point determines a value wine or an expensive one, though Ashenfelter and Steiman agree that most merchants use $50 and up as a starting point for the "fine wine" category. Still, price is not the guarantee: The track record is, and wine lovers can find that those in the $50 and up box are more likely to have proven themselves.

"Below $50 a bottle you're really rolling the dice in terms of red wine," Steiman says, adding that this "$50 floor" does not apply to whites, most of which are not typically thought of as collectibles. Most wines in this price range are not meant to cellar for a long time, though there are certainly surprise examples of those that may get better over time.

As is often the case with decision-making related to wine, a lot of it comes down to perception, Steiman says. Some red wines of small volume are collectible (such as grand cru Burgundies), but a lot more red wines are considered ageable than are whites. Some whites are thought of as collectibles, but they represent a small percentage by volume. Grand Cru white Burgundy is the most prominent category of white collectibles, Steiman says. Rieslings also age well for improved drinking, especially those from Alsace, Germany, and Australia, but they do not make great investments and are considered more as "insider" wines. Sweet whites such as Sauternes and Barsac are definitely considered collectible, especially Chateau d'Yquem, which Steiman says can age for more than a century, followed by Burgundy's Grand Crus and to a much lesser extent Riesling. Sweet Rieslings, especially Trockenbeerenauslese from Germany, are very expensive, very rare, very fine and ageable, and therefore collectible, but there is so little produced that they don't comprise a real market.

"Like any other collectible, wine has its specialists, and there are those who have great collections of all these white types because they love them, not because they expect great monetary returns on investment," Steiman says.

As president of the American Association of Wine Economists (AAWE), an organization dedicated to encouraging dialogue about all economic aspects of wine-related economic research and analyses, including production, pricing, labeling,

"THE FIRST THING YOU HAVE TO ASK YOURSELF IS HOW IMPORTANT IT IS THAT YOU BE ABLE TO EARN A DOLLAR PROFIT OUT OF INVESTING IN WINE. AND THAT'S TRICKY TO DO."

and distribution, Ashenfelter says that, while the wine industry may not always agree with him and fellow AAWE wine economists, especially when it comes to wine ratings and how they affect pricing, a large body of evidence suggests that more expensive wines do not taste better.

In a sample of more than 6,000 blind tastings, Robin Goldstein and his colleagues found, in an article published in the AAWE's *Journal of Wine Economics*, that the correlation between price and overall rating is small and negative for wines that were not expensive, suggesting that individuals on average enjoy more expensive wines slightly less. "Our results indicate that both the prices of wines and wine recommendations by experts may be poor guides for non-expert wine consumers," the paper summarizes. It also found that individuals who are unaware of the price do not derive more enjoyment from more expensive wine, though for those with wine training there are indications of a positive relationship between price and enjoyment.

Robert Hodgson, a retired Humboldt State University statistics professor and owner of Fieldbrook Winery, a small operation that produces about 10 wines each year and sells 1,500 cases, has written two important papers in the *Journal of Wine Economics* addressing the idea that back-to-back judgments of the same wine, by the same wine expert, vary so widely that the ratings on which they base their reputations are nothing more than a

2000 Chateau Petrus. Petrus is a typical purchase of serious investors.

powerful illusion. Although he agrees that the idea of a system in which industry experts cull through the countless numbers of wines to offer consumers shortcuts for selecting what fits their drinking or investing needs, the current process is badly flawed.

Wondering how wines, such as his own, can win a gold medal at one competition, and "end up in the pooper" at others, Hodgson took a course in wine judging, which led to him being on the advisory board for the California State Fair wine competition, North America's oldest and most prestigious. In this capacity, he was given permission to run a controlled scientific study of the tastings, conducted in the same manner as traditional ones.

Using the same blind tasting process as the actual competition, in his first study, for four years Hodgson served panels of 70 judges from the California State Fair Wine Competition about 100 wines over a two-day period. Each wine was presented to each judge three times, each time drawn from the same bottle.

Hodgson was astonished. Judges' wine ratings typically varied by four points, plus or minus, on a standard ratings scale running from 80 to 100. It was not unlikely that a wine rated 91 in one tasting would then be rated an 87 or 95 during the next. Some of the judges did much worse, and only about one in 10 regularly rated the same wine within a range of two points. Any consistent performance in judging, he found, could be explained by the laws of chance.

At the same time, as he started playing with the data, he noticed that the probability of a wine winning a gold medal in one competition and winning nothing in others was high. To test the idea, Hodgson restricted his attention to wines entering a certain number of competitions. The bar graph representing the number of wines winning was almost identical to the one that would result from repeatedly flipping a coin.

What this means, Ashenfelter says, is that while most wine enthusiasts exaggerate the differences between one wine and another, and put enormous credence into what the wine experts recommend, "There's very little evidence that they can tell you anything beyond the obvious."

Although the subjectivity of ratings continues to be met with skepticism, wine investors can rest assured that the numbers

GRGICH HILLS WINERY

Photos courtesy of Grgich Hills Winery

Mike Grgich's life reads like a Hollywood script (and in fact, his career was featured in George Taber's book, *Judgment of Paris*, about the 1976 Paris Tasting): Born in Croatia, one of 11 children, studied winemaking and viticulture at the University of Zagreb and then had to leave to escape communism. He eventually arrived in Napa Valley in August 1958, just in time for crush to begin. He has worked for some of the legends of Napa Valley: Lee Stewart, of the original Souverain Cellars; Brother Timothy at Christian Brothers; then for almost nine years for André Tchelistcheff at Beaulieu Vineyards; joining Robert Mondavi; and then winemaker at Chateau Montelena, where the chardonnay he crafted won the famed 1976 Paris Tasting, before starting his own winery. On Independence Day, July 4th, 1977, Mike Grgich and Austin Hills broke ground in Rutherford to build Grgich Hills Cellar.

Mike is still an innovator – all of the winery's wines are estate grown and all of

its vineyards are certified organic and Biodynamic. As part of the winery's efforts to be sustainable, Grgich Hills' converted to solar power in 2006. In recognition of his significant contributions to the wine industry, Mike was elected to the Vintner's Hall of Fame in 2008.

The winery remains family owned and operated with Mike assisted by his daughter, Violet Grgich, who is Vice President of Operations, and his nephew, Ivo Jeramaz, who is Vice President of Vineyards and Production. For more information, visit **www.grgich.com**.

never lie. And the truth they've been telling for the past several years is that wine is, in fact, a good investment.

The number of people genuinely investing in wine – that is, buying with an eye to selling it, rather than drinking it – is still tiny, but probably growing, and how much they have in holdings is also a mystery.

"The scale of wine investments is miniscule," Ashenfelter says. Although nobody knows how many collectors and investors there are, estimates of investment range from $100 million – considered negligible in the world of investing – to $500 million. The only certain numbers are how much wine is produced and how much is consumed, though it is impossible to determine how much is invested.

A research paper published in 2009 and updated this year by University of Fribourg economics professor Jean-Philippe Weisskopf and co-author Philippe Masset is the talk on the streets among serious investors worldwide. "Raise Your Glass: Wine Investment and the Financial Crisis," reviews how wine auction prices performed from 1996-2009 to determine if wine was a better investment than shares during this period, which includes two significant economic boom phases (1996-2001, 2003-2007) as well as two major economic and financial crises (2001-2003, 2007-2009).

In the most recent recession, the Wine Spectator Auction Index fell from 332.85 in the first half of 2008 to a low of 256.44 in the first half of 2009. It has since recovered to 313.22. In 2001, it fell from 171.57 to 153.94 in 2003, indicating that, like most consumables, fine and rare wines do not altogether hold their own during economic downtimes.

"Our findings show that the inclusion of wine in a portfolio and, especially more prestigious wines, increases the portfolio's returns while reducing its risk, particularly during the financial crisis," and the wine indexes show that prices have held steady for the top collectible wines, the study concludes. Although this is good news for those who have been investing in wine, Ashenfelter says it is bad news for fine wine collectors because investors are driving prices up so high that top wines are often unavailable to all but the very wealthy, who are not even necessarily wine lovers.

Part of this trend includes the growth of wine investing in Asia, as auction houses follow the wealth.

"It used to be that the number of people with $1 billion wasn't a lot, but the growth of the number of wealthy people in the world is what keeps the prices high," Ashenfelter says.

HOW TO

TIPS ON STARTING YOUR OWN WINE COLLECTION

Collecting wine is a lot more complicated than buying a Rolls-Royce or Bentley.

"There are all kinds of variables you need to consider before you raise your paddle," says Peter Meltzer, author of "Keys to the Cellar: Strategies and Secrets of Wine Collecting," and auction correspondent for *Wine Spectator*. Whether bidding on a wine that is intended to be an investment, or collecting for your own personal enjoyment, there are several tips for easing into the world of wine collecting so you have enough expertise to take part in bidding at auctions and buying wines online or through specialty wine retailers. Starting a wine collection is more than just a matter of grabbing a few bottles as

the conveyor belt rolls on by: It's understanding vintage variations, knowing how to find out what's in demand, what is not performing, or understanding how to use tasting notes.

"Not all harvests are created equally," Meltzer says. What this means is that to be good at buying wine, a novice collector must understand that success requires part science, a bit of economics, and a lot of been-around-the-track.

Focusing on the buyer who is collecting wine to drink – whether that means tonight with dinner or after it has had a few years to mature – Meltzer offers these tips for buying wines at auctions that will provide the foundation of a starter collection to fit various budget and lifestyle needs:

• Auctions are not for the impatient. They are typically all-day affairs, but they are casual, free, include pre-sale tastings, and present a good opportunity to learn.
• Get the auction catalog in advance and study it so that you have a plan. This helps control purchases and will allow you to compare retail prices and auction estimates to determine where it makes the most sense to buy, though Meltzer says auctions will usually be the better buy.
• If you're attending a wine auction for the first time, do not bid. Watch and learn so you understand the bidding steps and how the auctioneer proceeds. Otherwise, you run the risk of missing out on good deals or getting into a bidding war for which you will not be prepared.
• Egos tend to run amok at auctions. To avoid getting caught in the fray, submit absentee bids online or by fax, which allows you to set a ceiling price and avoid making emotional buys.
• Unlike a piece of artwork, most wine is not unique and will come around again – often in

the same month. Don't worry about missing out; there's a good chance you'll have another opportunity to bid on it in the immediate future.
• Review tasting notes from wine writers and critics, which in the absence of actually trying the wine yourself will give you others' impressions of wines they have drunk. *Wine Spectator* is known for its database of more than 200,000 wines that are scored on a straightforward 100-point basis.
• Be aware of vintage variations. Even with a great vintage, some wines are better than others. A great source of information is *Wine Spectator*'s Auction Price Database, available through www.winespectator.com, which includes information on more than 12,000 different collectible wines and includes how they've performed on a quarterly basis, prices and percentage changes, and data that indicates what's on the rise and what's not doing as well.
• If you're collecting with hopes of making money on your investment, buy at the top end of the wines you like. Consider this: During the second quarter of 2010, Château

Lafite Rothschild 1982 hit $4,840 per bottle at a Zachys auction. Last year it was selling for $2,000. When it first came on the market in 1983, a case sold for $390.
• Most established auction houses are on the East Coast, though Meltzer also recommends several others that are held across the country throughout the year. For your next road trip, plan the itinerary so you can work in some of these noteworthy auctions: New York – Acker Merrall & Condit, Aulden Cellars-Sotheby's, Christie's, Zachys, Morrell & Company; Chicago – Hart Davis Hart Wine Company; San Francisco – Bonhams & Butterfields. Zachys also frequently hosts auctions in Los Angeles and Las Vegas.

VIDEO WITHOUT COMPROMISE

Theater design and architecture by TK Theaters, NY,NY.

Runco is the enthusiast's choice

If you are looking for an unparalleled cinema experience in your home, look no further than the craftsmanship of Runco. Combining leading display engineering with luxurious design and personalization, our custom projector and flat panel video products raise the bar of excellence for every room of your home. A standard we first set when we began pioneering the home theater over twenty years ago. The legacy we continue with every new, award-winning innovation, including 3D. Runco puts you in the driver's seat of an entertainment experience like no other.

Allow us to introduce you to a Runco Authorized Dealer or provide you additional information at our client concierge desk at 1-800-237-8626 or via email at concierge@Runco.com.

Visit www.RuncoConcierge.com

RUNCO

2011

DESK DIARY

27
MONDAY

It is the function of vice
to keep virtue within
reasonable grounds.
SAMUEL BUTLER

28
TUESDAY

29
WEDNESDAY

30
THURSDAY

31
FRIDAY

New Year's Eve

1
SATURDAY

New Year's Day

2
SUNDAY

3
MONDAY

Women are like elephants.
They are interesting to
look at, but I wouldn't want
to own one.
W.C. FIELDS

4
TUESDAY

5
WEDNESDAY

6
THURSDAY

7
FRIDAY

8
SATURDAY

9
SUNDAY

10
MONDAY

*More than kisses,
letters mingle souls.*
JOHN DONNE

11
TUESDAY

12
WEDNESDAY

13
THURSDAY

14
FRIDAY

15
SATURDAY

16
SUNDAY

17
MONDAY

Martin Luther
King, Jr. Day

To ignore evil is to become
an accomplice to it.
MARTIN LUTHER KING, JR.

18
TUESDAY

19
WEDNESDAY

20
THURSDAY

21
FRIDAY

22
SATURDAY

23
SUNDAY

24
MONDAY

Words, like eyeglasses, blur
everything that they do
not make clear.
JOSEPH JOUBERT

25
TUESDAY

26
WEDNESDAY

27
THURSDAY

28
FRIDAY

29
SATURDAY

30
SUNDAY

31
MONDAY

Everyone hears only what
he understands.
GOETHE

1
TUESDAY

2
WEDNESDAY

3
THURSDAY

4
FRIDAY

5
SATURDAY

6
SUNDAY

7
MONDAY

Oh, to be only half as
wonderful as my child
thought I was when he
was small, and only half as
stupid as my teenager now
thinks I am.
REBECCA RICHARDS

8
TUESDAY

9
WEDNESDAY

10
THURSDAY

11
FRIDAY

12
SATURDAY

13
SUNDAY

14
MONDAY

VALENTINE'S DAY

Love consists in this, that
two solitudes protect
and touch and greet each
other.
RAINER MARIA RILKE

15
TUESDAY

16
WEDNESDAY

17
THURSDAY

18
FRIDAY

19
SATURDAY

20
SUNDAY

21
MONDAY

PRESIDENTS' DAY

He has a right to criticize,
who has a heart to help.
ABRAHAM LINCOLN

22
TUESDAY

23
WEDNESDAY

24
THURSDAY

25
FRIDAY

26
SATURDAY

27
SUNDAY

28
MONDAY

*If you want a thing done,
go – if not, send.*
BENJAMIN FRANKLIN

1
TUESDAY

2
WEDNESDAY

3 THURSDAY

4 FRIDAY

5 SATURDAY

6 SUNDAY

7
MONDAY

Chance is the pseudonym
of God when he did not
want to sign.
ANATOLE FRANCE

8
TUESDAY

9
WEDNESDAY

10
THURSDAY

11
FRIDAY

12
SATURDAY

13
SUNDAY

Daylight Savings Time
Begins

14
MONDAY

*If you shoot at mimes,
should you use a silencer?*
STEVEN WRIGHT

15
TUESDAY

16
WEDNESDAY

17
THURSDAY

St. Patrick's Day

18
FRIDAY

19
SATURDAY

20
SUNDAY

21
MONDAY

I think we consider too much the good luck of the early bird and not enough the bad luck of the early worm.
FRANKLIN D. ROOSEVELT

22
TUESDAY

23
WEDNESDAY

24
THURSDAY

25
FRIDAY

26
SATURDAY

27
SUNDAY

28
MONDAY

The human race is faced
with a cruel choice: work or
daytime television.
UNKNOWN

29
TUESDAY

30
WEDNESDAY

31
THURSDAY

1
FRIDAY

April Fool's Day

2
SATURDAY

3
SUNDAY

4
MONDAY

The great use of life is to spend it for something that will outlast it.
WILLIAM JAMES

5
TUESDAY

6
WEDNESDAY

7
THURSDAY

8
FRIDAY

9
SATURDAY

10
SUNDAY

11
MONDAY

Providence protects children and idiots. I know because I have tested it.
MARK TWAIN

12
TUESDAY

13
WEDNESDAY

14
THURSDAY

15
FRIDAY

16
SATURDAY

17
SUNDAY

18
MONDAY

It's hard to be funny
when you have to be clean.
MAE WEST

19
TUESDAY

20
WEDNESDAY

21
THURSDAY

22
FRIDAY

23
SATURDAY

24
SUNDAY

Easter

25
MONDAY

*Love your enemies in case
your friends turn out to be
a bunch of bastards.*
R.A. DICKSON

26
TUESDAY

EARTH DAY

27
WEDNESDAY

28
THURSDAY

29
FRIDAY

30
SATURDAY

1
SUNDAY

2
MONDAY

Always look out for Number One and be careful not to step in Number Two.
RODNEY DANGERFIELD

3
TUESDAY

4
WEDNESDAY

5
THURSDAY

6
FRIDAY

7
SATURDAY

8
SUNDAY

MOTHER'S DAY

9
MONDAY

It's not what you are, it's what you don't become that hurts.
OSCAR LEVANT

10
TUESDAY

11
WEDNESDAY

12
THURSDAY

13
FRIDAY

14
SATURDAY

15
SUNDAY

16
MONDAY

I don't consider myself
bald. I'm simply taller than
my hair.
TOM SHARP

17
TUESDAY

18
WEDNESDAY

19
THURSDAY

20
FRIDAY

21
SATURDAY

22
SUNDAY

23
MONDAY

Life is ours to be spent, not
to be saved.
D.H. LAWRENCE

24
TUESDAY

25
WEDNESDAY

MAY 2011

26 THURSDAY

27 FRIDAY

28 SATURDAY

29 SUNDAY

30
MONDAY

SMALL CAPS Memorial Day

*Love is an exploding cigar
we willingly smoke.*
LYNDA BARRY

31
TUESDAY

1
WEDNESDAY

2
THURSDAY

3
FRIDAY

4
SATURDAY

5
SUNDAY

6
MONDAY

All men make mistakes,
but married men find out
about them sooner.
RED SKELTON

7
TUESDAY

8
WEDNESDAY

9
THURSDAY

10
FRIDAY

11
SATURDAY

12
SUNDAY

13
MONDAY

Parents are not interested
in justice, they are
interested in quiet.
BILL COSBY

14
TUESDAY

15
WEDNESDAY

16
THURSDAY

17
FRIDAY

18
SATURDAY

19
SUNDAY

FATHER'S DAY

20
MONDAY

I'm not confused, I'm just well-mixed.
ROBERT FROST

21
TUESDAY

22
WEDNESDAY

23
THURSDAY

24
FRIDAY

25
SATURDAY

26
SUNDAY

27
MONDAY

Education is not the filling
of a pail, but the lighting
of a fire.

WILLIAM BUTLER YEATS

28
TUESDAY

29
WEDNESDAY

30
THURSDAY

1
FRIDAY

2
SATURDAY

3
SUNDAY

4
MONDAY

INDEPENDENCE DAY

The only normal people
are the ones you don't
know very well.
JOE ANCIS

5
TUESDAY

6
WEDNESDAY

7
THURSDAY

8
FRIDAY

9
SATURDAY

10
SUNDAY

11
MONDAY

The best way to destroy
an enemy is to make him
a friend.
ABRAHAM LINCOLN

12
TUESDAY

13
WEDNESDAY

JULY 2011

14
THURSDAY

15
FRIDAY

16
SATURDAY

17
SUNDAY

18
MONDAY

The magic of the tongue
is the most dangerous of
all spells.
EDWARD BULWER-LYTTON

19
TUESDAY

20
WEDNESDAY

21
THURSDAY

22
FRIDAY

23
SATURDAY

24
SUNDAY

25
MONDAY

Only Irish coffee provides in a single glass all four essential food groups: alcohol, caffeine, sugar, and fat.

ALEX LEVINE

26
TUESDAY

27
WEDNESDAY

28
THURSDAY

29
FRIDAY

30
SATURDAY

31
SUNDAY

1
MONDAY

I base my fashion taste on what doesn't itch.
GILDA RADNER

2
TUESDAY

3
WEDNESDAY

4
THURSDAY

5
FRIDAY

6
SATURDAY

7
SUNDAY

8
MONDAY

He who endeavors to
control the mind by force
is a tyrant, and he who
submits is a slave.
ROBERT G. INGERSOLL

9
TUESDAY

10
WEDNESDAY

11
THURSDAY

12
FRIDAY

13
SATURDAY

14
SUNDAY

15
MONDAY

I would rather make my name than inherit it.
WILLIAM MAKEPEACE
THACKERAY

16
TUESDAY

17
WEDNESDAY

18
THURSDAY

19
FRIDAY

20
SATURDAY

21
SUNDAY

22
MONDAY

Start every day off with a
smile and get it over with.
W.C. FIELDS

23
TUESDAY

24
WEDNESDAY

25
THURSDAY

26
FRIDAY

27
SATURDAY

28
SUNDAY

29
MONDAY

*I am two fools, I know, for
loving, and saying so.*
JOHN DONNE

30
TUESDAY

31
WEDNESDAY

1
THURSDAY

2
FRIDAY

3
SATURDAY

4
SUNDAY

5
MONDAY
LABOR DAY

They say hard work never hurt anybody, but I figure why take the chance.
RONALD REAGAN

6
TUESDAY

7
WEDNESDAY

8
THURSDAY

9
FRIDAY

10
SATURDAY

11
SUNDAY

12
MONDAY

Flirtation – attention
without intention.
MAX O'NEIL

13
TUESDAY

14
WEDNESDAY

15
THURSDAY

16
FRIDAY

17
SATURDAY

18
SUNDAY

19
MONDAY

A good cigar is as great a comfort to a man as a good cry is to a woman.
EDWARD BULWER-LYTTON

20
TUESDAY

21
WEDNESDAY

22
THURSDAY

23
FRIDAY

24
SATURDAY

25
SUNDAY

26
MONDAY

It is impossible to enjoy
idling thoroughly unless
one has plenty of work
to do.

JEROME K. JEROME

27
TUESDAY

28
WEDNESDAY

29
THURSDAY

30
FRIDAY

1
SATURDAY

2
SUNDAY

3
MONDAY

Some fellows pay a compliment like they expected a receipt.
KIN HUBBARD

4
TUESDAY

5
WEDNESDAY

6
THURSDAY

7
FRIDAY

8
SATURDAY

9
SUNDAY

10
MONDAY

Columbus Day
OBSERVED

Only the shallow know
themselves.
OSCAR WILDE

11
TUESDAY

12
WEDNESDAY

13
THURSDAY

14
FRIDAY

15
SATURDAY

16
SUNDAY

17
MONDAY

*If I die, I forgive you:
if I recover, we shall see.*
SPANISH PROVERB

18
TUESDAY

19
WEDNESDAY

20
THURSDAY

21
FRIDAY

22
SATURDAY

23
SUNDAY

24
MONDAY

The most essential gift for a good writer is a built-in, shockproof shit detector. This is the writer's radar and all great writers have had it.

ERNEST HEMINGWAY

25
TUESDAY

26
WEDNESDAY

27
THURSDAY

28
FRIDAY

29
SATURDAY

30
SUNDAY

31
MONDAY

Halloween

Sleeping is no mean art.
For its sake one must stay
awake all day.
FRIEDRICH NIETZSCHE

1
TUESDAY

2
WEDNESDAY

3
THURSDAY

4
FRIDAY

5
SATURDAY

6
SUNDAY
Daylight Savings
Time ends

7
MONDAY

*We never touch
but at points.*
RALPH WALDO EMERSON

8
TUESDAY

9
WEDNESDAY

10
THURSDAY

11
FRIDAY

Veterans Day

12
SATURDAY

13
SUNDAY

14
MONDAY

I am a part of all that
I have met.
ALFRED, LORD TENNYSON

15
TUESDAY

16
WEDNESDAY

17
THURSDAY

18
FRIDAY

19
SATURDAY

20
SUNDAY

21
MONDAY

If you drink, don't drive.
Don't even putt.
DEAN MARTIN

22
TUESDAY

23
WEDNESDAY

24
THURSDAY

Thanksgiving Day

25
FRIDAY

26
SATURDAY

27
SUNDAY

28
MONDAY

I do beseech you to direct your efforts more to preparing youth for the path and less to preparing the path for the youth.
BEN LINDSEY

29
TUESDAY

30
WEDNESDAY

1
THURSDAY

2
FRIDAY

3
SATURDAY

4
SUNDAY

5
MONDAY

Fashions, after all, are
only induced epidemics.
GEORGE BERNARD SHAW

6
TUESDAY

7
WEDNESDAY

8
THURSDAY

9
FRIDAY

10
SATURDAY

11
SUNDAY

12
MONDAY

And all the loveliest
things there be
Come simply,
so it seems to me.
EDNA ST. VINCENT MILLAY

13
TUESDAY

14
WEDNESDAY

15
THURSDAY

16
FRIDAY

17
SATURDAY

18
SUNDAY

19
MONDAY

Tradition is a guide
and not a jailer.
W. SOMERSET MAUGHAM

20
TUESDAY

HANUKKAH BEGINS
(AT SUNDOWN)

21
WEDNESDAY

22
THURSDAY

23
FRIDAY

24
SATURDAY

Christmas Eve

25
SUNDAY

Christmas Day

26
MONDAY

I forget what I was taught.
I only remember
what I have learnt.
PATRICK WHITE

27
TUESDAY

28
WEDNESDAY

29
THURSDAY

30
FRIDAY

31
SATURDAY
New Year's Eve

1
SUNDAY
New Year's Day

2
MONDAY

There are two kinds of people, those who finish what they start and so on.
ROBERT BYRNE

3
TUESDAY

4
WEDNESDAY

5
THURSDAY

6
FRIDAY

7
SATURDAY

8
SUNDAY

2012 CALENDAR

JANUARY

MON	TUE	WED	THU	FRI	SAT	SUN
						1
2	3	4	5	6	7	8
9	10	11	12	13	14	15
16	17	18	19	20	21	22
23/30	24/31	25	26	27	28	29

FEBRUARY

MON	TUE	WED	THU	FRI	SAT	SUN
	1	2	3	4	5	
6	7	8	9	10	11	12
13	14	15	16	17	18	19
20	21	22	23	24	25	26
27	28	29				

MARCH

MON	TUE	WED	THU	FRI	SAT	SUN
			1	2	3	4
5	6	7	8	9	10	11
12	13	14	15	16	17	18
19	20	21	22	23	24	25
26	27	28	29	30	31	

APRIL

MON	TUE	WED	THU	FRI	SAT	SUN
						1
2	3	4	5	6	7	8
9	10	11	12	13	14	15
16	17	18	19	20	21	22
23/30	24	25	26	27	28	29

MAY

MON	TUE	WED	THU	FRI	SAT	SUN
	1	2	3	4	5	6
7	8	9	10	11	12	13
14	15	16	17	18	19	20
21	22	23	24	25	26	27
28	29	30	31			

JUNE

MON	TUE	WED	THU	FRI	SAT	SUN
			1	2	3	
4	5	6	7	8	9	10
11	12	13	14	15	16	17
18	19	20	21	22	23	24
25	26	27	28	29	30	

JULY

MON	TUE	WED	THU	FRI	SAT	SUN
						1
2	3	4	5	6	7	8
9	10	11	12	13	14	15
16	17	18	19	20	21	22
23/30	24/31	25	26	27	28	29

AUGUST

MON	TUE	WED	THU	FRI	SAT	SUN
	1	2	3	4	5	
6	7	8	9	10	11	12
13	14	15	16	17	18	19
20	21	22	23	24	25	26
27	28	29	30	31		

SEPTEMBER

MON	TUE	WED	THU	FRI	SAT	SUN
					1	2
3	4	5	6	7	8	9
10	11	12	13	14	15	16
17	18	19	20	21	22	23
24	25	26	27	28	29	30

OCTOBER

MON	TUE	WED	THU	FRI	SAT	SUN
1	2	3	4	5	6	7
8	9	10	11	12	13	14
15	16	17	18	19	20	21
22	23	24	25	26	27	28
29	30	31				

NOVEMBER

MON	TUE	WED	THU	FRI	SAT	SUN
		1	2	3	4	
5	6	7	8	9	10	11
12	13	14	15	16	17	18
19	20	21	22	23	24	25
26	27	28	29	30		

DECEMBER

MON	TUE	WED	THU	FRI	SAT	SUN
					1	2
3	4	5	6	7	8	9
10	11	12	13	14	15	16
17	18	19	20	21	22	23
24/31	25	26	27	28	29	30

To Convert	Multiply by
Inches to Centimeters	2.5400
Centimeters to Inches	0.3937
Feet to Meters	0.3048
Meters to Feet	3.2810
Yards to Meters	0.9144
Meters to Yards	1.0940
Miles to Kilometers	1.6090
Kilometers to Miles	0.6214
Inches^2 to Centimeters^2	6.4520
Centimeters^2 to Inches^2	0.1550
Meters^2 to Feet^2	10.7600
Feet^2 to Meters^2	0.0929
Yards^2 to Meters^2	0.8361
Meters^2 to Yards^2	1.1960
Miles^2 to Kilometers^2	2.5900
Kilometers^2 to Miles^2	0.3861
Acres to Hectares	0.4047
Hectares to Acres	2.4710
Inches^3 to Centimeters^3	16.3900
Centimeters^3 to Inches^3	0.0610
Feet^3 to Meters^3	0.0283
Meters^3 to Feet^3	35.3100
Yards^3 to Meters^3	0.7646
Meters^3 to Yards^3	1.3080
Inches^3 to Liters^3	0.0163
Liters^3 to Inches^3	61.0300
Gallons to Liters	4.5460
Liters to Gallons	0.2200
Grains to Grams	0.0648
Grams to Grains	15.4300
Ounces to Grams	28.3500
Grams to Ounces	0.0352
Pounds to Grams	453.6000
Grams to Pounds	0.0022
Pounds to Kilograms	0.4536
Kilograms to Pounds	2.2050
Tons to Kilograms	1016.0000
Kilograms to Tons	0.0009

TEMPERATURE

To convert Fahrenheit to Celsius (Centigrade) subtract 32, multiply by 5, and divide by 9.

To convert Celsius to Fahrenheit multiply by 9, divide by 5, and add 32.

A Fahrenheit degree is smaller than a Celsius degree, one Fahrenheit degree being $5/9$ of a Celsius degree.

The freezing point of water is 32°F, 0°C. The boiling point is 212°F, 100°C.

LIQUIDS

1 gallon (British Imperial) = 1.20 gallons (U.S.)

1 gill = 4 fluid ounces

1 quart (British) = 1.20 quarts (U.S.)

1 quart (U.S.) = 67.2 cubic inches

1 tablespoon = .5 fluid ounce

1 teaspoon = 1.33 fluid drams

1 dekaliter = 10 liters

1 pint = .5 quart

MISCELLANEOUS

1 cubit = 18 inches

1 fathom = 6 feet

1 league = 3 miles

1 nautical mile = 1.15 miles

1 light-year = 5.88 trillion miles

1 hand = 4 inches

1 degree (geographical) = 69.05 miles

1 point (typography) = .01 inch

1 gross hundredweight = 112 pounds

1 gross ton = 2,240 pounds

1 carat = 200 milligrams

SELECTED ROLLS-ROYCE AND BENTLEY DEALERSHIPS

ARIZONA

Rolls-Royce Motor Cars/Bentley
Scottsdale
7111/7171 E. Chauncey Ln.
Phoenix, AZ 85054
480.538.4300

CALIFORNIA

Rolls-Royce Motor Cars/Bentley
Beverly Hills
8845/8833 West Olympic Blvd.
Beverly Hills, CA 90211
310.659.4050 or 888.294.1133

Symbolic Motor Car Co.
7440 La Jolla Blvd.
La Jolla, CA 92037
858.454.1800

Rolls-Royce Motor Cars Los Gatos
620 Blossom Hill Rd.
Los Gatos, CA 95030
877.217.8637

Bentley Los Gatos
66 East Main St.
Los Gatos, CA 95030
408.354.4000

Rolls-Royce Motor Cars
Newport Beach
4040 Campus Dr.
Newport Beach, CA 92660
949.515.6200

Bentley Newport Beach
445 East Pacific Coast Hwy.
Newport Beach, CA 92660
949.673.0900

Rusnak Automotive Group
337/285 West Colorado Blvd.
Pasadena, CA 91105
626.449.0770 or 626.229.2544

Desert European Motorcars Ltd.
71-387 Highway 111
Rancho Mirage, CA 92270
760.773.5000

Bentley San Francisco
999 Van Ness Ave.
San Francisco, CA 94109
415.351.5102

COLORADO

Bentley Denver
1480 E. County Line Rd.
Highlands Ranch, CO 80126
303.730.7340

CONNECTICUT

Miller Motorcars Inc.
275 West Putnam Ave.
Greenwich, CT 06830
203.661.4430 or 203.661.3100

FLORIDA

Rolls-Royce Motor Cars/Bentley
Fort Lauderdale
200 East Sunrise Blvd.
Fort Lauderdale, FL 33304
954.779.2009

Rolls-Royce Motor Cars/
Bentley Miami
2060/2020 Biscayne Blvd.
Miami, FL 33137
305.571.1205

Rolls-Royce Motor Cars/
Bentley Naples
900 Tamiami Trail North
Naples, FL 34102
239.263.6070 or 1.866.603.6025

Ultimate Motor Works Inc.
895 N. Ronald Reagan Blvd.
Longwood, FL 32750
407.339.3443

Rolls-Royce Motor Cars/Bentley
Tampa Bay
3333 Gandy Blvd.
Pinellas Park, FL 33781
727.822.2019 or 727.489.1470

Rolls-Royce Motor Cars/
Bentley Palm Beach
2901 Okeechobee Blvd.
West Palm Beach, FL 33409
561.684.6666 or 888.237.1051

GEORGIA

Rolls-Royce Motor Cars Atlanta
3040 Piedmont Rd.
Atlanta, GA 30305
404.237.6200

Bentley Atlanta
1305 Old Roswell Rd.
Alpharetta, GA 30004
678.352.3572

HAWAII

Bentley Honolulu
720 Kapiolani Blvd.
Honolulu, HI 96813
808.377.4614

ILLINOIS

Steve Foley Inc./
Bentley Northbrook
100 N. Skokie Blvd.
Northbrook, IL 60062
847.564.4090 or 888.265.0590

Bentley Oak Brook
330 Ogden Ave.
Downers Grove, IL 60515
630.324.6554

INDIANA

Bentley Zionsville
360 South First St.
Zionsville, IN 46077
317.873.2360

MARYLAND

Rolls-Royce Motor Cars
Washington, D.C.
7020 Arlington Rd.
Bethesda, MD 20814
301.986.8800

Bentley Bethesda
4937 Bethesda Ave.
Bethesda, MD 20814
888.707.4422

MASSACHUSETTS

Herb Chambers Rolls-Royce
Motor Cars of New England/Bent-
ley Boston
533 Boston Post Rd.
Wayland, MA 01778
508.401.2700 or 508.650.0020

MICHIGAN

Rolls-Royce Motor Cars
Michigan/ Bentley Troy
1755 C/B Maplelawn Dr.
Troy, MI 48084
866.534.2087 or 248.341.8022

MINNESOTA

Bentley Minneapolis
13708 Wayzata Blvd.
Minnetonka, MN 55305
952.797.1777

MISSOURI

Rolls-Royce Motor Cars/
Bentley St. Louis
9/1 Arnage Blvd.
Chesterfield, MO 63005
636.449.0000

NEVADA

Rolls-Royce Motor Cars/Bentley
Las Vegas
2550 South Jones
Las Vegas, NV 89146
702.932.7100

NEW JERSEY

F.C. Kerbeck & Sons/Bentley
Palmyra New Jersey
100 Route 73 North
Palmyra, NJ 08065
856.829.8200

Paul Miller Rolls-Royce/
Bentley Parsipanny
250 Route 46
Parsipanny, NJ 07054
973.575.7755

NEW YORK

Rolls-Royce Motor Cars Long Island
45 S. Service Rd.
Plainview, NY 11803
516.592.6700

Bentley Long Island
115 South Service Rd.
Jericho, NY 11753
866.708.0050

Rolls-Royce Motor Cars/
Bentley Manhattan
270 Eleventh Ave.
New York, NY 10001
212.594.6200 or 888.590.1780

NORTH CAROLINA

Rolls-Royce Motor Cars Raleigh
5601 Capital Blvd.
Raleigh, NC 27616
919.876.5432

Bentley High Point
1730 North Main St.
High Point, NC 27262
336.884.1100

OHIO

Midwestern Auto Group/
Bentley Columbus
6335 Perimeter Loop Rd.
Dublin, OH 43017
614.717.4840 or 614.889.2571

PENNSYLVANIA

Ascot Imported Cars Inc.
418 Walnut St.
Sewickley, PA 15143
412.741.3300

Bentley Pittsburgh
2150 West Liberty Ave.
Pittsburgh, PA 15226
866.923.6010

RHODE ISLAND

Bentley Providence –
Inskip Autogroup
1515 Bald Hill Rd.
Warwick, RI 02886
401.821.1510

TEXAS

Bentley Austin
12989 North U.S. Hwy 183,
Building B100
Austin, TX 78750
512.236.8539

Rolls-Royce Motor Cars/
Bentley Dallas
5300 Lemmon Ave.
Dallas, TX 75209
214.443.8240 or 214.849.5300

Rolls-Royce Motor Cars/
Bentley Houston
1530 West Loop South
Houston, TX 77027
713.850.1530

UTAH

Bentley Salt Lake City
155 South Frontage Rd.
Centerville, UT 84014
801.298.5300

WASHINGTON

Bentley Bellevue
1882 136th Place NE, Suite 107
Bellevue, WA 98005
425.646.3111

CANADA

Bentley Calgary
150 Glendeer Circle SE
Calgary, Alberta T2H 2V4
001.403.208.6262

Bentley Montreal
8255 Rue Bougainville
Montreal, Quebec H4P 2T3
514.334.9910

Rolls-Royce Motor
Cars/Bentley Toronto
740 Dupont Rd.
Toronto, Ontario
M6G 1Z6
416.530.1880

Rolls-Royce Motor Cars
Vancouver
1717 West 5th Ave.
Vancouver, British Columbia
V6J 3H5
604.659.3200

Bentley Vancouver
1730 Burrard St.
Vancouver, British Columbia V6J
3G7
604.738.5577

MEXICO

Rolls-Royce Motor Cars
Mexico City
Av. Presidente Masaryk 60
Col. Polanco C.P. 11560
Mexico City D.F., Mexico
+52.55.5255.1552

Bentley Polanco
Campos Eliseos 247
Col. Polanco
Mexico City, Mexico
11560, Mexico
+52.55.52803535

ART, MUSEUMS & COLLECTIBLES

Altermann Galleries:
505.983.1590
www.altermann.com

Art Basel Miami Beach (ABMB):
212.627.1654
www.artbaselmiamibeach.com

Art Gallery of Ontario:
416.979.6648
www.ago.net

Asian Art Museum
of San Francisco:
415.581.3500
www.asianart.org

Atlas Galleries:
Chicago, IL
800.423.7635
800.545.2929
www.atlasgalleries.com

Bonhams & Butterfields:
www.bonhams.com/us

Bart Walter Studio:
www.bartwalter.com

Christie's:
212.492.5485
www.christies.com

Dale Chihuly:
www.chihuly.com

EYE Photographic Workshops:
www.eyephotographicworkshops.
com

Frank & Frank Sporting
Collectibles:
Howell, New Jersey
732.938.2988
www.frankandfrankdecoys.com

Gallery 1870:
Yountville, CA
800.322.1870
www.gallery1870.com

Gerald Peters Gallery:
505.954.5700
212.628.9760
www.gpgallery.com

Guyette & Schmidt, Inc.:
www.guyetteandschmidt.com

Joel Oppenheimer Inc.:
312.642.5300
843.853.1100
www.audubonart.com

Lillian Nassau Gallery:
212.759.6062
www.lilliannassau.com

Lladro:
www.lladro.com

Market Gallery:
416.392.7604
www.stlawrencemarket.com/
gallery

Mary Boone Gallery:
www.maryboonegallery.com

National Geographic Museum:
202.857.7588
www.nationalgeographic.com/
museum/

Nedra Matteucci Galleries:
505.982.4631
www.matteucci.com

Shelburne Museum:
Shelburne, VT
802.985.3346
www.shelburnemuseum.org

Sotheby's:
www.sothebys.com

Victor Issa Studios:
Loveland, CO
800.720.ISSA
www.victorissa.com

The Ward Museum of Wildfowl
Art:
Salisbury, MD

410.742.4988
www.wardmuseum.org

Xanadu Gallery:
415.392.9999
www.xanadugallery.us

Yvon Lambert Gallery:
212.242.3611
www.yvon-lambert.com

AUTOMOTIVE

A.J. Glew:
www.ajglew.co.uk

Access Custom Garage Doors:
800.994.3643
www.accessgaragedoor.com

Avenue Mailorder:
+44.149.448.3906
www.avenuemail.com

Bensport Spares:
802.253.9256

Covercraft:
405.238.9651
www.covercraft.com

Dennison-Jayne Motors:
West Chester, PA
610.436.8668
www.dennisonjaynemotors.com

Ecosse Moto Works:
303.246.3080
www.ecossemoto.com

Exotic Car Transport:
Orlando, FL
407.293.9524
800.766.8797
www.exoticcartransport.com

Fiennes Restoration:
+44.136.781.0438
www.fiennes.co.uk

Forgiato Inc.:
Sun Valley, CA
818.771.9779

www.forgiato.com

The Frawley Company:
Parkesburg, PA
610.857.1099
www.thefrawleycompany.com

Garia:
San Antonio, TX
210.481.5500
www.garia.dk

Harman Becker:
www.harmanbecker.com

The Kexby Limited Company:
Williamsburg, VA
757.258.8550
www.easirider.com

Lista:
508.429.1350
877.465.4782
+41.71.649.21 11
www.listainternational.com

Madera Concepts:
805.962.1579
800.800.1579
www.maderaconcepts.com

NavTV:
866.477.3336
www.nav-tv.com

P. & A. Wood:
44.(0)1371.870.848
www.pa-wood.co.uk

Premier Garage:
www.premiergarage.com

Revolution Lifts:
800.604.3359
www.revolutionlifts.com

Ristes Motors:
www.ristesmotors.co.uk
+44.115.978.5834

Rolls-Royce and Bentley
Specialists Association (RRBSA):
www.rrbsa.co.uk

Rotary Lift Inc.:
812.273.1622
800.640.5438
www.rotarylift.com

Samstag Sales:
Carthage, TN
615.735.3388
www.samstagsales.com

Select 1 Transport:
877.810.9700
www.select1.com

Stanley Mann Racing Ltd.:
44.(0).1923.852505
www.stanleymann.com

Thomas Hamann Rare and Exotic
Automobiles:
786.254.7007
www.hamannclassiccars.com

Ultimate Garage:
201.262.0412
www.ultimategarage.com

Vintage and Auto Rebuilds:
Chardon, OH
440.285.2742
www.ghostparts.com

The Vintage Garage:
802.253.9256
www.vintagegaragevt.com

Vista Upholstery Enterprises:
www.upholster.com

ELECTRONICS

Apple:
www.apple.com

CAT MBX:
888.HEAR.CAT
www.catmbx.com

Crestron Electronics:
www.crestron.com

Crystal Cable:
www.crystalcable.com

Custom Electronic Design and
Installation Association:
317.328.4336
800.669.5329
www.cedia.net

Dell:
www.dell.com

Dream Vision:
www.audioplusservices.com

Dynaudio North America:
www.dynaudiousa.com

Escient: www.escient.com

Harman International:
www.harman.com

Hewlett-Packard
www.hp.com

IBM:
www.ibm.com

Intel:
www.intel.com

Kharma International BV:
www.kharma.com

Lexicon:
www.lexicon.com

McIntosh:
www.mcintoshlabs.com

Marsh Sound Design:
www.marshsounddesign.com

MBL of America:
www.mbl-hifi.com

Meridian America:
www.meridian-audio.com

Mirage Loudspeakers:
1.866.428.2122
www.miragespeakers.com

Motorola:
www.motorola.com

Panasonic:
www.panasonic.com

Pioneer:
www.pioneerelectronics.com

Runco:

1.800.237.8826

www.runco.com

Sony:

www.sony.com

Vertu Americas:

www.vertu.com

Von Gaylord Audio:

800.783.7360

www.vongaylordaudio.com

Wisdom Audio:

Carson City, NV

775.887.8850

www.wisdomaudio.com

Yamaha: www.yamaha.com/yec

FOOD & DRINK

Acker Merrall & Condit:

New York, NY

212.787.1700

www.ackerwines.com

Aulden Cellars-Sotheby's:

New York, NY

212.894.1990

www.sothebyswine.com

Blicker-Pierce-Wagner-Gregory

Wine Merchants (BPWine):

707.967.0240

www.bpwine.com

Catapano Dairy in Peconic:

Peconic, NY

631.7655.8042

www.capatanodairyfarm.com

Chop't:

www.chopt.com

Christie's International Wine

Department:

www.christies.com/departments/

wine

Cowgirl:

www.cowgirlcreamery.com

Cypress Grove:

Arcata, CA

707.825.1100

www.cypressgrovechevre.com

FAIR. Quinoa Vodka

www.fairtradespirits.com

Foppiano Vineyards:

Healdsburg, CA

707.433.7272

www.foppiano.com

Gentleman's Jack Daniels:

www.jdsinglebarrel.com

Germain-Robin:

800.782.8145

www.germain-robin.com

The Glenlivet:

www.theglenlivet.com

Grey Goose:

www.greygoosevodka.com

Grgich Hills Estate:

Rutherford, CA

800.532.3057

www.grgich.com

Hart Davis Hart Wine Company:

Chicago, IL

312.482.9996

www.hdhwine.com

Hennessy:

www.hennessy.com

Kobe Beef America:

541.923.9664

www.kobe-beef.com

Krug Champagne:

www.krug.com

K&L Wine Merchants (San

Francisco):

www.klwines.com

Lobel's of New York:

212.737.1372

800.556.2357

877.783.4512

www.lobels.com

The Macallan:

www.themacallan.com

Melissa's/World Variety Produce:

Los Angeles, CA

800.588.0151

www.melissas.com

Mendis Brandy:

www.mendisbrandy.com

Morrell & Company:

New York, NY

212.688.9370

800.969.4637

www.morrellwine.com

Morrison Bowmore Distillers Ltd.:

www.bowmore.com

Napa Valley Harvest:

707.252.9463

www.winecountrykitchens.com

Sherry-Lehmann Wine & Spirits:

New York, NY

212.838.9285

www.sherry-lehmann.com

Sherwin Family Vineyards:

St. Helena, CA

707.963.1154

www.sherwinfamilyvineyards.com

Shinn Estate Vineyards:

Mattituck, NY

631.804.0367

www.shinnestatevineyards.com

Slow Food International:

Bra (Cuneo), Italy

+39.0172.419611

www.slowfood.com

Slow Food Nation:

510.893.2386

www.slowfoodnation.org

Slow Food USA:

718.260.8000

www.slowfoodusa.org

St. George Spirits:

Alameda, CA

510.769.1601

www.stgeorgespirits.com

Starbucks:

www.starbucks.com

Tazo:

www.tazo.com

TransFair USA:

www.transfairusa.org

Tsar Nicoulai Caviar:

San Francisco, CA

415.543.3007

1.800.952.2842

www.tsarnicoulai.com

Wallenford Coffee:

Kingston, Jamaica

876.923.5850.9

www.wallenford.com

Whole Foods:

www.wholefoodsmarket.com

Zachys Wine & Liquor:

www.zachys.com

HEALTH & BEAUTY

Jan Marini Skin Research:

800.347.2223

www.janmarini.com

La Prairie:

800.821.5718

www.laprairie.com

Pevonia:

1.800.PEVONIA

www.pevonia.com

HOME

A BOHEME Design, LLC:

Rosemary Beach, FL

850.231.6803

www.abohemedesign.com

Abramson Teiger Architects:

Culver City, CA

310.838.8998

www.abramsonteiger.com

Anichini:

800.553.5309

www.anichini.com

Clive Christian Home:

www.clive.com

Dean & Deluca:

800.221.7714

www.deananddeluca.com

ENERGY STAR:

www.energystar.gov

Engineered Environments:

West Palm Beach, FL

561.282.4111

www.eeigc.net

Frette:

800.353.7388

www.frette.com

E.S. Kluft & Company:

909.373.4211

www.kluftmattress.com

Gill Metal Fab:

Brockton, MA

508.580.4445

www.gillmetal.com

Grohe:

www.grohe.com

Hahn's Woodworking:

Branchburg, NJ

908.722.2742

www.hahnswoodworking.com

Herman Miller, Inc.:

www.hermanmiller.com

Ironies.:

Berkeley, CA

510.644.2100

www.ironies.com

Jim Thompson:

800.262.0336

www.jimthompsonfabrics.com

Knoll, Inc.:

www.knoll.com

LandDesign:

www.landdesign.com

Lee Jofa:

www.leejofa.com

Norris Broyles Architects, Inc.:

Atlanta, GA

404.257.1430

www.norrisbroyles.com

Olivier Gagnère:

www.gagnere.net

Plato Woodwork:

Plato, MN

800.328.5924

www.platowoodwork.com

Runco:

www.runco.com

Sferra:

www.sferralinens.com

Smarthome.com:

800.762.7846

www.smarthome.com

Thermador (BSH Home Appliance):

www.thermador.com

Yves Delorme:

800.322.3911

www.yvesdelorme.com

HOTELS & ACCOMMODATIONS

Amanresorts

www.amanresorts.com

Banyan Tree Hotels & Resorts
www.banyantree.com

Best Western
www.bestwestern.com

Fairmont Hotels and Resorts
1.800.257.7544
www.fairmont.com

Hilton Hotels & Resorts
www1.hilton.com

Hyatt
www.hyatt.com

InterContinental Hotels & Resorts
www.ichotelsgroup.com

Marriott
www.marriott.com

The Ritz-Carlton
www.ritzcarlton.com

Rixos Hotels
www.rixos.com

Singita Game Reserves
27.21.683.3424
www.singita.com

Wynn Resorts
www.wynnresorts.com

HOTELS & ACCOMMODA-TIONS INSIDE U.S.:

ARIZONA
Adobe Grand Villas:
Sedona, AZ
928.203.7616
866.900.7616
www.adobegrandvillas.com
Seven Canyons:
Sedona, AZ
866.367.8844
www.sevencanyons.com

CALIFORNIA
Hotel Bel-Air:
Los Angeles, CA
310.472.1211
www.hotelbelair.com
Hotel Union Square:
415.397.3000
www.hotelunionsquare.com
Westin St. Francis Hotel:
415.397.7000
www.westinstfrancis.com
Resort at Squaw Creek:
Olympic Valley, CA
530.583.6300
866.635.7937
www.squawcreek.com
Vacation Palm Springs:
Palm Springs, CA
760.778.7832
800.590.3110
www.vacationpalmsprings.com

COLORADO
The Broadmoor:
Colorado Springs, CO
719.577.5775
866.837.9520
www.broadmoor.com

FLORIDA
Grove Isle:
Coconut Grove, Miami, FL
800.884.7683
www.groveisle.com
Mandarin Oriental Miami
Miami, FL
305.913.8383
www.mandarinoriental.com
Ritz-Carlton Amelia Island:
904.277.1100

www.ritzcarlton.com/en/
Properties/AmeliaIsland/default.
htm
The Setai:
Miami Beach, FL
305.520.6000
www.setai.com

LOUISIANA
Hotel Monteleone:
New Orleans, LA
504.523.3341
www.hotelmonteleone.com
The Lafayette Hotel:
New Orleans, LA
504.524.4441
Renaissance Arts Hotel:
New Orleans, LA
504.613.2330
Soniat House:
New Orleans, LA
504.522.0570
800.544.8808
www.soniathouse.com
Windsor Court Hotel:
504.523.6000
New Orleans, LA
888.596.0955
www.windsorcourthotel.com

MICHIGAN
The Grand Hotel:
800.33.GRAND
www.grandhotel.com

MONTANA
Papoose Creek Lodge:
Cameron, MT
406.682.3030
888.674.3030

www.papoosecreek.com

NEW YORK
Fairmont - The Plaza N.Y.:
212.759.3000
888.850.0909
www.theplaza.com
The Whiteface Lodge:
Lake Placid, NY
518.523.0500
800.903.4045
www.thewhitefacelodge.com

NEVADA
Bellagio:
Las Vegas, NV
702.693.7111
www.bellagio.com
The Four Seasons Hotel
– Las Vegas:
702.632.5000
800.819.5053
www.fourseasons.com/lasvegas
The Las Vegas Hilton:
Las Vegas, NV
702.732.5111
888.732.7117
www.lvhilton.com
Mandalay Bay:
Las Vegas, NV
702.632.7777
877.632.7800
www.mandalaybay.com
MGM Grand:
Las Vegas, NV
877.880.0880
www.mgmgrand.com
The Venetian:
Las Vegas, NV
702.414.1000

www.venetian.com

TEXAS
The Driskill Hotel:
Austin, TX
512.474.5911
800.252.9367
www.driskillhotel.com
The Lancaster:
Houston, TX
713.228.9500
www.thelancaster.com
The Mansion on Turtle Creek:
Dallas, TX
214.559.2100
www.mansionturtlecreek.com

UTAH
Red Mountain Spa
St. George, UT
877.246.4453
www.redmountainspa.com
Resorts West:
Park City, UT
435.655.7006
1.877.214.0102
www.resortswest.com
Stein Eriksen Lodge:
Park City, UT
435.649.3700
www.steinlodge.com

VERMONT
The Equinox:
Manchester Village, VT
800.362.4747
www.equinoxresort.com
Green Mountain Inn:
Stowe, VT
802.253.7301

800.253.7302
www.gminn.com
The Woodstock Inn and Resort:
Woodstock, VT
802.457.1100
800.448.7900
www.woodstockinn.com

VIRGINIA
The Inn at Little Washington:
Washington, VA
540.675.3800
www.theinnatlittlewashington.com
The Jefferson Hotel:
Richmond, VA
804.788.8000
www.jeffersonhotel.com

WASHINGTON
The Fairmont Olympic Hotel Seattle:
206.621.1700
1.888.363.5022
www.fairmont.com/seattle
Bonneville Hot Springs Resort & Spa:
North Bonneville, WA
509.427.7767
866.459.1678
www.bonnevilleresort.com
The Sorrento Hotel:
Seattle, WA
206.622.6400
www.hotelsorrento.com

WASHINGTON, D.C.
Four Seasons Hotel Washington, DC:
202.342.0444
www.fourseasons.com/washington
Sofitel Lafayette Square:
Washington, D.C.
202.730.8800

WYOMING
Hotel Terra Jackson Hole:
Teton Village, WY
307.739.4000
www.hotelterrajacksonhole.com
Three Forks Ranch:
Savery, WY
970.583.7396
www.threeforks.com

**HOTELS &
ACCOMMODATIONS
OUTSIDE U.S.**
AUSTRALIA
Arajilla Retreat:
1.800.063.928
61.0.2.6583.2622
www.lordhowe.com.au
Orpheus Island Resort:
61.7.4777.7377
www.orpheus.com.au

BELIZE
Chaa Creek:
877.709.8708
www.chaacreek.com

CANADA
Auberge Saint-Antoine:
418.692.2211
888.692.2211
www.saint-antoine.com
Caesars Windsor:
1.800.991.8888
www.caesarswindsor.com
Château Bonne Entente:
800.463.4390
www.chateaubonneentente.com
Fairmont Le Château

Frontenac:
418.692.3861
www.fairmont.com/frontenac
The Four Seasons – Yorkville:
416.964.0411
www.fourseasons.com/toronto
Loews Hôtel Le Concorde:
800.23.LOEWS
loewshotels.com

COSTA RICA
Lapa Rios Ecolodge:
001.506.2735.5130
www.laparios.com

ENGLAND
The Capital Hotel in London:
44.0.20.7589.5171
www.capitalhotel.co.uk

GREECE
Capsis Hotels and Resorts:
www.capsis.com

HONG KONG
The Peninsula Hong Kong:
+852.2920.2888
hongkong.peninsula.com

JAMAICA
The Tryall Club:
www.tryallclub.com

JAPAN
The Peninsula Tokyo:
+813.6270.2888
tokyo.peninsula.com

MEXICO
Casa Dorada:

Los Cabos, Mexico
866.448.0151
www.casadoradaloscabos.com
Hacienda Tres Rios:
800.494.9173
www.haciendatresrios.com
Mision del Sol Resort & Spa:
Cuernavaca, Mexico
866.875.0380
www.misiondelsol.com
The Royal Cancun & Playa del
Carmen
800.760.0944
www.realresorts.com

MEXICO
Fiesta Americana Grand Los
Cabos Golf Resort & Spa:
1.877.927.7666
www.fiestaamericanagrand.com

MOROCCO
Riad El Fenn:
212.524.44.1210
www.riadelfenn.com

SAINT MARTIN
La Samanna:
590.590.87.64.00
800.237.1236
www.lasamanna.com

**SAINT VINCENT AND THE
GRENADINES**
The Mustique Company Ltd.:
784.488.8000
www.mustique-island.com

SOUTH AFRICA
Mount Nelson Hotel:

Cape Town, South Africa
800.237.1236
www.mountnelson.co.za
The Westcliff Hotel:
Johannesburg, South Africa
800.237.1236
www.westcliff.co.za

SPAIN
Barcelo Asia Gardens Hotel &
Thai Spa:
34.966.81.84.00
www.asiagardens.es

SRI LANKA
Jetwing Hotels:
www.jetwinghotels.com

SWITZERLAND
Badrutt's Palace:
41.0.81.837.1000
www.badruttspalace.com

THAILAND
Evason Hideaway Hua Hin:
+66.0.32.632.111
www.sixsenses.com/evason-hua-
hin/index.php

TURKEY
Hotel Empress Zoe:
90.212.518.25.04
www.emzoe.com

UNITED ARAB EMIRATES
Ottoman Palace:
Dubai
www.ottomanpalacedubai.com
www.rixos.com

**LUXURY TRANSPORTATION
& ACCESSORIES**
Air Harrods:
+44.0.1279.660.800
www.airharrods.com
Amazing Charters:
British Virgin Islands
704.257.47.66
www.amazingcharters.com
Bombardier FlexJet:
Quebec, Canada
800.flexjet
www.flexjet.com
Bombardier Skyjet:
888.275.9538
www.skyjet.com
Cessna:
www.cessna.com
Citation Shares:
Greenwich, CT
www.citationshares.com
Delta Air Elite:
800.927.0927
877.DAE.JETS
www.AirElite.com
Emirates:
www.emirates.com
Fleetwood Enterprises:
www.fleetwoodrv.com
Jet Aviation:
Privileged Travel
www.jetaviation.com/privi-
legedtravel
Liberty Coach:
800.332.9877
www.libertycoach.com
Lufthansa:
www.lufthansa-usa.com
Marquis Jet:
1.866.JET.1400

www.marquisjet.com
NetJets:
877.356.5823
www.netjets.com
Oceanco Yachts:
www.oceancoyacht.com
Optimum Jet Experts:
888.809.JET2
www.optimumjetexperts.com
PrivatSea Yachting:
+30.211.600.7000
www.privatseayachting.com
Qatar Airways:
www.qatarairways.com
Singapore Airlines:
www.singaporeair.com

PERSONAL STYLE
Balenciaga:
www.balenciaga.com
Barneys New York:
www.barneys.com
Bergdorf Goodman:
New York, NY
888.774.2424
www.bergdorfgoodman.com
Billy Reid:
www.billyreid.com
Breitling:
www.breitling.com
Brooks Brothers:
800.274.1815
www.brooksbrothers.com
Burberry:
www.burberry.com
Calvin Klein Collection:
www.calvinkleincollection.com
Calypso Enfant & Bebe:
New York, NY

212.966.3234
Carl F. Bucherer:
800.395.4306
www.carl-f-bucherer.com
Carrera y Carrera:
800.CYC.8229
www.carreraycarrera.com
Cartier:
1.800.cartier
+44.0.208.080.0330
www.cartier.com
Cellini:
800.cellini
www.cellinijewelers.com
Chopard:
212.821.0300
+44.20.7439.3304
www.chopard.com
Christian Louboutin:
www.christianlouboutin.com
Cole, Rood & Haan:
www.colehaan.com
Cross:
800.282.7677
www.cross.com
Donald J Pliner:
888.307.1630
www.donaldjpliner.com
FAO Schwarz:
New York, NY
212.644.9400 ext. 4242
www.fao.com
Fendi:
www.fendi.com
Fred Leighton:
New York, NY
212.288.1872
Las Vegas, NV
(at the Bellagio)
702.693.7050

www.fredleighton.com
Giorgio Armani:
www.armani.com
Gucci:
www.gucci.com
Harry Winston:
Beverly Hills, CA
310.271.8554
www.harry-winston.com
Hublot/MDM:
www.hublot.com
J. Mavec & Co.:
New York, NY
212.517.7665
J.M. Weston:
www.jmweston.com
Jil Sander:
www.jilsander.com
Kara Ross:
www.kararossny.com
Kate Spade:
www.katespade.com
Kiton:
212.486.5250
www.kiton.it
La Perla:
www.laperla.com
Lester Lampert:
312.944.6888
www.lesterlampert.com
Lex Diamonds:
866.500.1539
www.lexdiamondwatch.com
Louis Vuitton:
www.louisvuitton.com
The Met Store:
800.468.7386
www.metmuseum.org/store/
index.asp
Missoni:

www.missoni.com
Montblanc:
www.montblanc.com
Neil Lane Jewelry:
Los Angeles, CA
310.275.5015
www.neillanejewelry.com
Neiman Marcus:
888.888.4757
www.neimanmarcus.com
Nigel Cabourn:
www.cabourn.com
Oscar de la Renta:
www.oscardelarenta.com
Panama Hat Co. of the Pacific:
Kailua, HI
808.262.2892
888.658.6500
www.brentblack.com
Pierre Hardy:
www.pierrehardy.com
Porthault:
212.688.1660
www.dporthaultparis.com
Saks Fifth Avenue:
New York, NY
212.753.4000
800.347.9177
www.saksfifthavenue.com
Simon Spurr:
www.spurr.tv
Smythson:
877.769.8476
www.smythson.com
Smithwick Dillon:
www.smithwickdillon.com
Stella McCartney:
www.stellamccartney.com
Stephen Russell:
New York, NY

212.570.6900
Tiffany & Co.:
New York, NY
212.755.8000
800.843.3269
www.tiffany.com
Tod's:
866.907.9720
www.tods.com
Van Cleef & Arpels:
800.VCA.5797
Zac Posen
www.zacposen.com

REAL ESTATE/HOME CONSTRUCTION

Engel & Völkers:
www.engelvoelkers.com
Remax (The Island):
Cayman Islands,
British West Indies
345.949.9772
www.theislandresort.ky
Re/Max Isla Bonita:
+501.624.5252
www.owninbelize.com
Ritz-Carlton
Residences Grand Cayman:
345.815.7777
www.residences-cayman.com
The Residences at the
Ritz-Carlton, Montreal:
1.877.748.9685
www.residences.ritzmontreal.
com/rl
The Residences at the Ritz-
Carlton, Toronto:
416.591.1000
866.651.6351
www.theresidencestoronto.com

Ritz-Carlton Residences Vail:
800.351.3679
www.theresidencesvail.com
Sotheby's International Realty
Jackson Hole:
www.sothebyshomes.com/jack-
sonhole
Starwood Vacation Ownership:
800.601.8699
www.starwoodvacationowner-
ship.com
The St. Regis
Residence Club New York:
866.776.9637
www.starwoodresidenceclub.com
West Indies Brokers:
345.943.9400
www.westindiesbrokers.com
Willis Allen:
877.515.7443
www.willisallen.com

SERVICES

Advanced Strategies Group:
877.274.0829
www.advancedstrategiesgroup.
com
Aquatic Art Technologies:
1.877.355.3991
www.aquaticarttechnologies.com
Bessemer Trust:
212.708.9100
www.bessemer.com
Blueprint Research and Design:
415.677.9700
www.blueprintrd.com
Coppertree Ltd.:
513.579.3531
www.coppertreeltd.com
Ensemble Capital

Management:
650.696.1240
www.ensemblecapital.com
Family Wealth Alliance:
630.260.1010
www.fwalliance.com
Heathmount International Ltd.:
858.349.7920 (San Diego)
978.457.9345 (Boston)
+44.788.789.2747 (London)
www.heathmount.com
Lauren Berger Collection:
888.522.1099
www.laurenberger-collection.com
Lifelock:
800.543.3562
www.lifelock.com
Madame Paulette:
New York, NY
347.689.7010
www.madamepaulette.com
Marsh Inc.:
212.345.6000
global.marsh.com
Pitcairn Financial Group:
800.211.1745
www.pitcairn.com
Rockefeller Financial:
212.549.5100
www.rockefellerfinancial.com
Selective Search Inc.:
www.selectivesearch-inc.com
312.396.1200
SkyMed Global:
800.475.9633
www.skymedglobal.com
Trusted ID:
888.548.7878
www.trustedid.com

Valenti International:
800.200.8253
www.valentiinternational.com
Vogel Consulting:
262.790.4960
www.vogelcg.com
We Invest Online:
630.413.4039
www.weinvestonline.com

SPORTS & RECREATION

Federation of International Polo:
+33 344 549 463
www.fippolo.com
Frontiers International:
800.245.1950
www.frontierstravel.com
Innovative Golf Systems:
1.866.286.9975
www.igolfsys.com
Isla Monita Fishing Lodge:
562.889.8200
www.islamonita.cl
J World Performance Sailing
School:
www.jworldschool.com
Kitty Hawk Kites:
877.FLY.THIS
www.kittyhawk.com
Motor Racing Heritage
Association Inc.:
mrhaweb.com
Raabe Racing Enterprises:
386.274.4676
www.raaberacing.com
Steiner Leisure:
www.steinerleisure.com
US Sailing:
401.683.0800
1.500.877.2451
www.ussailing.org

SPORTS EQUIPMENT

Krieghoff Gun Co:
800.73KGUNS
www.halkguns.com
Life Fitness:
800.527.6065
www.lifefitness.com
Oberwerk:
937.426.8892
866.244.2460
866.OBERWERK
www.oberwerk.com
www.bigbinoculars.com
Olhausen Billiards:
858.486.0761
800.866.4606
www.olhausenbilliards.com
Red Drum Tackle Shop:
252.995.5414
www.reddrumtackle.com
Völkl Sport America:
603.298.8032
www.volkl.com
Wagner Rods:
440.845.4415
www.wagnerrods.com
William Henry Knives:
503.434.9700
888.563.4500
www.williamhenrystudio.com

TRAVEL

Abercrombie & Kent:
800.554.7016
www.abercrombiekent.com
Adventure Associates:
877.500.9402
www.adventureassociates.com
Ahipara Travel:
64.9.446.6025
www.ahipara.com

Albuquerque Tourism Info:
800.284.2282
www.itsatrip.org
Asia Transpacific Journeys:
800.642.2742
www.southeastasia.com
Brendan Worldwide
Vacations:
800.421.8446
www.brendanvacations.com
Bridge & Wickers:
020.7483.6555
www.bridgeandwickers.co.uk
Butterfield & Robinson:
866.551.9090
800.67.81.14.77
www.butterfield.com
Cayman Island Department
of Tourism:
877.4.CAYMAN
www.caymanislands.ky
Cazenove+Loyd:
44.0.20.7384.2332
www.cazloyd.com
Cox & Kings:
1.800.999.1758
www.coxandkingsusa.com
Elegant Adventures:
800.451.4398
www.elegantadventures.com
Exeter International:
Tampa, FL
813.251.5355
800.633.1008
www.exeterinternational.com
Food & Wine Trails:
a division of HMS Travel,
800.367.5348
www.foodandwinetrails.com
iExplore:
800.iexplore

www.iexplore.com
International Wildlife
Adventures:
800.808.4492
www.wildlifeadventures.com
Ladatco Tours:
800.327.6162
305.854.8422
www.ladatco.com
Las Vegas Convention Center:
702.892.0711
www.lvcva.com
Le Marche travel information:
800.222.1111
www.le-marche.com
Mexico Tourism Board:
www.visitmexico.com
800.44.MEXICO
The Miami Beach
Convention Center:
305.673.7311
www.miamibeachconvention.com
Muddy York Walking Tours:
416.487.1.9017
www.muddyyorktours.com
Napa Valley Destination Council:
Napa, CA
707.226.5813
www.legendarynapavalley.com
National Geographic Expeditions:
1.888.966.8687
www.nationalgeographicexpeditions.com
National Golf Club:
877.992.9939
www.nationalgc.com
New Orleans Visitors Bureau:
800.672.6124
www.neworleanscvb.com
Nomadic Expeditions, Inc.:

609.860.9008
1.800.998.6634
www.nomaidcexpeditions.com
Orient-Express:
www.orient-express.com
Outer Banks Visitors Bureau:
877.629.4386
www.outerbanks.org
Passport in Time:
800.281.9176
www.passportintime.com
Quebec City and Area:
877.BONJOUR
www.quebecregion.com
Royal Shell Vacations:
800.656.9111
www.royalshell.com
The Selous Project:
255.767.755.537
www.selousproject.com
South Australian Tourism
Commission:
888.768.8428
www.southoz.com
Sustainable Travel
International:
www.sustainabletravel.com
Taiamai Tours Heritage Journeys:
64.9.405.9990
www.taiamaitours.co.nz
Tauck:
800.788.7885
www.tauck.com

TCS and Starquest Expeditions:
206.254.0228
1.800.454.4149
www.tcsandstarquestexpeditions.
com
TD Guides:
800.606.1255
www.td-guides.com
A Taste of
South Australia:
+61. 8. 83713553
www.tastesa.com.au
Toronto Tourism:
800.499.2514
www.torontotourism.com
Tourabout Adelaide:
+08.8333.1111
www.touraboutadelaide.com.au
Uncharted Africa Safari Co.:
27.0.11. 447.1605
www.unchartedafrica.com
Valerie Wilson
Travel, Inc.:
800.776.1116
212.532.3400
www.vwti.com
Washington, D.C. Tourist
Information:
800.422.8644
www.washington.org
White Desert:
416.862.2001
www.white-desert.com

BARCELÓ ASIA GARDENS HOTEL & THAI SPA

ALICANTE (SPAIN)

+34.966.81.84.00

WWW.ASIAGARDENS.ES

E. S. KLUFT & COMPANY, LLC

RANCHO CUCAMONGA, CA

909.373.4211

WWW.KLUFTMATTRESS.COM

WWW.AIRELOOM.COM

FIESTA AMERICANA GRAND LOS CABOS GOLF & SPA RESORT

CABO SAN LUCAS, B.C.S.

LOCAL: 52.624.1.45.6200

RESERVATIONS: 1.800.FIESTA1

WWWW.FIESTAMERICANAGRAND.COM

FOPPIANO VINEYARDS

HEALDSBURG, CA

707.433.7272

WWW.FOPPIANO.COM

MODULINE MODULAR ALUMINUM CABINETS

BROCKTON, MA 02301

TOLL FREE: 888.343.4463

WWW.MODULINEGARAGE.COM

GRGICH HILLS ESTATE

RUTHERFORD, CA

707.963.2784

800.532.3057

WWW.GRGICH.COM

GUYETTE & SCHMIDT, INC.

ST. MICHAELS, MD

410.745.0485

WWW.GUYETTEANDSCHMIDT.COM

HAHN WOODWORKING COMPANY INC.

BRANCHBURG, NJ 08876

908. 722.2742

WWW.HAHNSWOODWORKING.COM

LAUREN BERGER COLLECTION

NEW YORK, NY

888.LBC.1099

917.306.5600

WWW.LAURENBERGERCOLLECTION.COM

LLADRÓ

NEW YORK, NY

866.LLADRO 7

WWW.LLADRO.COM

MANDARIN ORIENTAL, MIAMI

MIAMI, FL

305.913.8383

TOLL FREE: 866.888.6780

WWW.MANDARINORIENTAL.COM/MIAMI

NETJETS INC.

COLUMBUS, OH

614.239.5500

WWW.NETJETS.COM

BRENT BLACK PANAMA HATS

KAILUA, HI

888.658.6500

808.262.2892

WWW.BRENTBLACK.COM

PLATO WOODWORK INC.

PLATO, MN

800.328.5924

WWW.PLATOWOODWORK.COM

RIXOS HOTELS

ANTALYA / TÜRKIYE

+90.242.323.2526

WWW.RIXOS.COM

ROYAL SHELL VACATIONS

SANIBEL, FL

LOCAL: 239.472.9111

TOLL FREE: 800.656.9111

WWW.ROYALSHELL.COM

SAFE
STRATEGICALLY ARMORED AND FORTIFIED ENVIRONMENTS

WASHINGTON, D.C.

LOS ANGELES, CA

202.484.9500

WWW.SAFE-US.COM

SHERWIN FAMILY VINEYARDS

ST. HELENA, CA

707.963.1154

WWW.SHERWINFAMILYVINEYARDS.COM

THERMADOR

HUNTINGTON BEACH, CA

800.735.4328

WWW.THERMADOR.COM

THE LODGE AND SPA AT THREE FORKS RANCH

SAVERY, WY

970.583.7396

WWW.THREEFORKSRANCH.COM

THE TRYALL CLUB

MONTEGO BAY
JAMAICA, WEST INDIES

RESERVATIONS & INFORMATION:
1.800.238.5290 OR 1.876.956.5660

WWW.TRYALLCLUB.COM

WALLENFORD COFFEE COMPANY

JAMAICA, WEST INDIES

876.923.5850.9

WWW.WALLENFORD.COM

WE INVEST ONLINE, INC.

LOCKPORT, IL

815.546.3459

WWW.WEINVESTONLINE.COM

WYNN LAS VEGAS AND ENCORE

LAS VEGAS, NV

702.770.7000

888.320.7123

WWW.WYNNLASVEGAS.COM

WWW.ENCORELASVEGAS.COM